NOTRE DAME MATHEMATICAL LECTURES

Number 10

TOPICS IN LOCAL ALGEBRA

LECTURES DELIVERED AT THE
UNIVERSITY OF NOTRE DAME

by

DR. JEAN DIEUDONNÉ

Professor of Mathematics, University of Nice, France

Edited and Supplemented by

DR. MARIO BORELLI

Assistant Professor of Mathematics, University of Notre Dame

NOTRE DAME, INDIANA

1967

Library of Congress Catalog Card Number: 67-30420
Printed in the United States of America

PREFACE

These are notes of lectures which I gave at the University of Notre Dame during the fall of 1966; they have been written and prepared for publication by Dr. M. Borelli, Assistant Professor at the University of Notre Dame, whom I heartily thank for the care with which he has accomplished his task and the many hours he has devoted to it.

The lectures were intended as an introduction to modern algebraic geometry, in order to familiarize with some of its most important concepts mathematicians who have had no previous contact with that theory. The scope of the book prevented me from giving anything like a complete exposition, and I have accordingly suppressed a large number of proofs, all of which can be found either in Bourbaki's "Algèbre commutative" or in Grothendieck's "Eléments de Géométrie algébrique". On the other hand, the proofs which are given have been made as explicit as possible, and Dr. Borelli has taken great pains to spell out many details which would be taken for granted by anybody having some familiarity with the material.

As the title indicates, the concepts which are studied are those which have to do with the properties of an algebraic variety (or scheme) at a point, or equivalently with the local ring of the scheme at that point. The most important of these concepts are dimension, depth, regularity, normality and completeness, and they are most of the time studied for noetherian local rings.

In the study of the dimension of a module M over a noetherian semi-local ring A (§1 and 2) we prove the Krull-Chevalley-Samuel theorem, which gives three different interpretations of dimension, namely as the Krull dimension, as the leading coefficient of the

Hilbert-Samuel polynomial, and as the smallest number of elements $x_1, \ldots, x_r$ of A such that the Module $M/x_1 M+\ldots+x_r M$ has finite length. The general form of the Hauptidealsatz is proved in §2.

§3 is devoted to the notion of depth and the study of the properties of Cohen-Macauley rings.

Regular rings are defined in §4. Here, in addition to giving the usual definition and properties of regular local rings, we characterize the regular local rings of classical Algebraic Geometry as those rings whose corresponding points are simple, i.e. the corresponding Jacobian matrix has maximal rank. The cohomological dimension of a ring is defined, and the Hilbert-Serre theorem concerning it is stated (but not proved). In this same §4 we characterize reduced and normal noetherian rings, the latter characterization due to Serre.

§5 concerns itself with the behavior of the above mentioned notions under local, flat morphisms, and in §6 we apply the results of §5 to the study of the completion and normalization of a noetherian local ring. The main results of §6 are Cohen's Structure Theorem for noetherian complete local rings, and Nagata's theorem that every noetherian, complete, local integral domain is Japanese. The notes end with the definition of Grothendieck's excellent rings and the statement of the theorem that localizations of finitely generated algebras over excellent rings are again excellent.

I have tried to give to the notes a geometrical flavor, in as much as possible, by examining, with examples and figures, most of the above notions in the context of classical Algebraic Geometry over the complexes.

CONTENTS

PREREQUISITES

The essential prerequisites for these notes are contained in Bourbaki, "Commutative Algebra", Chapters I through IV. Results from Chapters V through VII will sometimes (but not often) be referred to. We shall denote them throughout by B.C.A., so that when we write, say, Proposition 4, B.C.A., III, 3, 2 we mean proposition 4 to be found in Bourbaki's "Commutative Algebra", Chapter III, §3, no 2.

We begin by recalling some of the elementary fundamental notions of Commutative Algebra and modern Algebraic Geometry. No attempt at proofs will be made here, most proofs being available either from the above mentioned chapters of Bourbaki, or from Grothendieck's EGA.

We consider only commutative rings A with unit element, and only ring homomorphisms such that $1 \rightsquigarrow 1$.

Unless otherwise specified, the rings considered will be <u>noetherian</u>. This means that the set of ideals of A satisfies the ascending chain condition, or equivalently, that every ideal of A admits a finite basis.

We call A <u>semi-local</u> if it has a finite number of maximal ideals. If A has a unique maximal ideal (when no danger of ambiguity exists, ideal will always mean proper ideal), A is said to be a <u>local ring</u>.

We call A a <u>Jacobson ring</u> if every prime ideal $\mathfrak{p} \subset A$ is the intersection of the maximal ideals containing it, $\mathfrak{p} = \bigcap_{\mathfrak{m} \supset \mathfrak{p}} \mathfrak{m}$.

The <u>radical of A</u>, rad(A), is defined as the intersection of all the maximal ideals of A, $\mathrm{rad}(A) = \bigcap_{\mathfrak{m} \subset A} \mathfrak{m}$.

The <u>nilradical of A</u>, $\mathfrak{n}(A)$, is the intersection of all prime ideals of A, $\mathfrak{n}(A) = \bigcap_{\mathfrak{p} \text{ prime}} \mathfrak{p}$. $\mathfrak{n}(A)$ is easily seen to consist precisely of the nilpotent elements of A. When $\mathfrak{n}(A) = (0)$ i.e. when A has no nilpotent elements, A is said to be reduced. If A is a Jacobson ring rad(A) = $\mathfrak{n}(A)$, but already when A is a nontrivial local ring (i.e. not a field) rad(A) = $\mathfrak{m} \neq \mathfrak{n}(A)$ in general, where $\mathfrak{m}$ denotes the unique maximal ideal of A.

One result which will be used often is the following

Nakayama's Lemma. Let A be a ring, M, N two finitely generated A-modules. Let $u: M \to N$ be an A-morphism, and let $\mathfrak{a}$ be an ideal of A with $\mathfrak{a} \subset \text{rad}(A)$. If $u \otimes \text{id}_{A/\mathfrak{a}} : M \otimes (A/\mathfrak{a}) \to N \otimes (A/\mathfrak{a})$ is surjective, so is u.

Let A be a ring, S a multiplicatively closed subset of A. On the set-theoretical product AxS define the following equivalence relation

$$(a, s) \sim (a', s') \iff \text{there exists } s'' \in S \text{ with } s''(as' - a's) = 0.$$

One easily checks that the following operations

$$(a, s) + (a', s') = (as' + a's, ss')$$
$$(a, s) \cdot (a', s') = (aa', ss')$$

define a ring structure on the set of equivalence classes of AxS. We denote such ring by A_S, and call it the localization of A at S. We denote the equivalence class of (a, s) by a/s. The homomorphism $\tau: A \to A_S$ defined by $\tau(a) = as/s$ (for any $s \in S$) turns A_S into an A-module. We caution that τ need not be injective.

Let M be an A-module. We define $M_S = A_S \otimes_A M$. It is easy to check that M_S can be obtained also by repeating verbatim the above procedure for the construction of A_S, simply substituting M for A.

In the category of rings and ring homomorphisms, A_S can be more simply defined as follows:

> the localization of A at S consists of a ring C, and a homomorphism $\rho \in \mathrm{Hom}(A, C)$ such that for all rings B the function $\mathrm{Hom}(C, B) \to \mathrm{Hom}(A, B)'$ is bijective, where $\mathrm{Hom}(A, B)'$ consists of all those morphisms $u \in \mathrm{Hom}(A, B)$ such that all elements of u(S) are units in B.

In most applications to Algebraic Geometry the set S is of one of two types. In the first, S consists of the non negative powers of an element $t \in A$, and we write A_t instead of A_S. In the second type, S is the complement of a prime ideal $\mathfrak{p}$ of A. In this case we use the notation $A_{\mathfrak{p}}$ instead of $A_{A-\mathfrak{p}}$.

Let M be a finitely generated A-module. We define

$$\mathrm{Ass}(M) = \{\mathfrak{p} \text{ a prime ideal of } A \mid \mathfrak{p} \text{ is the annihilator of some } x \in M, x \neq 0\}$$

$$\mathrm{Supp}(M) = \{\mathfrak{p} \text{ a prime ideal of } A \mid A_{\mathfrak{p}} \otimes_A M \neq 0\}.$$

Ass(M) is a finite set when A is noetherian, and is related to Supp(M) by the following property: the minimal primes of Ass(M) coincide with the minimal primes of Supp(M). We call Ass(M) the <u>set of associated ideals of M</u>, and Supp(M) the <u>support of M</u>.

In the case that M = A the following statements are true:

1) Ass(A) = the prime ideals (isolated and imbedded) corresponding to (0).

2) $\bigcup_{\mathfrak{p} \in \mathrm{Ass}(A)} \mathfrak{p}$ = the set of zero divisors.

3) {the minimal primes of Supp(A)} = {the isolated primes of (0)} = {the minimal primes of A}.

4) $\mathfrak{n}(A) = \bigcap_{\mathfrak{p} \in \mathrm{Ass}(A)} \mathfrak{p}$.

We give some examples of the above notions, again without any attempts at proofs.

The <u>local rings</u> most commonly met in Algebraic Geometry are of the form $A_{\mathfrak{p}}$ where $\mathfrak{p}$ is a prime ideal of A. It is immediate to check that the complement of $\mathfrak{p}A_{\mathfrak{p}}$ in $A_{\mathfrak{p}}$ consists of units, whence $\mathfrak{p}A_{\mathfrak{p}}$ is the unique maximal ideal of $A_{\mathfrak{p}}$.

An example of a <u>Jacobson ring</u> is given by $A/\mathfrak{p}$, where A is a finitely generated algebra over an algebraically closed field k, and $\mathfrak{p}$ is a prime ideal of A.

Finally, we leave as an exercise to the reader to prove that, if M is a finitely generated A-module with annihilator $\mathfrak{a}$, then Ass(M) = {the prime ideals corresponding to an irredundant primary decomposition of $\mathfrak{a}$}.

GEOMETRIC NOTIONS

Let A be a ring. We recall that <u>Spec(A)</u> is defined, as a set, to consist of all the prime ideals $\mathfrak{p}$ of A. Such set is made into a topological space by defining a subbasis of open sets (which actually turns out to be a basis) as follows:

we define, for $t \in A$, $D(t) = \{ \mathfrak{p} \in \mathrm{Spec}(A) \mid t \notin \mathfrak{p} \}$,

and consider the collection $(D(t))_{t\in A}$ as the subbasis in question. (That it is a basis is easily seen from $D(st) = D(s) \cap D(t)$, $s, t \in A$.) The resulting topology on Spec(A) is usually called the Zariski topology.

Equivalently, we can define the Zariski topology by determining what the closed subsets are. Here we take any ideal $\mathfrak{a} \subset A$ and define

$$V(\mathfrak{a}) = \{ \mathfrak{p} \in \mathrm{Spec}(A) \mid \mathfrak{a} \subset \mathfrak{p} \}.$$

The collection of sets $(V(\mathfrak{a}))$ is easily seen to satisfy the axioms of closed sets in a topology, and one then shows that

$$\mathrm{Spec}(A) - D(t) = V(tA)$$
$$\mathrm{Spec}(A) - V(\mathfrak{a}) = \bigcup_{t \notin \mathfrak{a}} D(t)$$

whence the two topologies are actually the same.

Since A is noetherian, Spec(A) is a <u>noetherian topological space</u>, i.e. the open subsets of Spec(A) satisfy the maximal condition, or, equivalently, the closed subsets of Spec(A) satisfy the minimal condition. Hence Spec(A) is the finite union of its irreducible components.

We caution that Spec(A) is however highly non-Hausdorff. In fact one easily sees that $\mathfrak{a} \subset \mathfrak{b} \Rightarrow V(\mathfrak{a}) \supset V(\mathfrak{b})$, hence a point $\mathfrak{p} \in \mathrm{Spec}(A)$ has in general a closure distinct from $\mathfrak{p}$, in fact equal to $V(\mathfrak{p})$. $\mathfrak{p}$ is hence a closed point if, and only if, the ideal $\mathfrak{p}$ is maximal. However, given two distinct points $\mathfrak{p}$, $\mathfrak{q}$ of Spec(A), we can find an element $t \in A$ which belongs to one but not the other of the two ideals (we can't tell which though), whence an open subset D(t) which contains one point but not the other. In other words Spec(A) is a T_0 (Kolmogoroff) topological space. We also remark that the only closed, irreducible components of Spec(A) are precisely the closures of the minimal prime ideals of A, and that the only closed irreducible subsets of Spec(A) are precisely the subsets of the form $V(\mathfrak{a})$, where $\mathfrak{a}$ is any ideal in A with a prime radical. In fact $V(\mathfrak{a}) = V(\sqrt{\mathfrak{a}})$, for $\mathfrak{a} \subset A$.

With every ring A we have made correspond a certain topological space, Spec(A). We ask the question: given the topological space Spec(A), can we recover A? Unfortunately not, since, e.g., all fields have homeomorphic Spectra. The notion which is missing, in order to obtain an adequate dictionary between the algebraic and the geometric languages is the notion, due to Serre, of the <u>sheaf of local rings</u> of Spec(A).

This is a sheaf $\tilde{A}$ which can be defined in one of two equivalent ways

1) As a presheaf $\tilde{A}(D(t)) = A_t \quad t \in A$
2) As an espace étale, the stalk $\tilde{A}_{\mathfrak{p}}$ of $\tilde{A}$ over the point $\mathfrak{p} \in \mathrm{Spec}(A)$ is given by $\tilde{A}_{\mathfrak{p}} = A_{\mathfrak{p}}$.

One can easily prove that $A_{\mathfrak{p}} = \varinjlim_{t \notin \mathfrak{p}} A_t$, where the homomorphisms $A_s \to A_{st}$ are given by $a/s^n \rightsquigarrow at^n/(st)^n$. Hence the two definitions are indeed equivalent.

We now have associated with every ring A two objects,

namely the topological space Spec(A) and the sheaf of local rings $\tilde{A}$ over Spec(A). Given the pair (Spec(A), $\tilde{A}$), it is now easy to recover A, namely $A = A_1 = \tilde{A}(D(1)) = \tilde{A}(\mathrm{Spec}(A))$, which is the totality of sections of $\tilde{A}$ over Spec(A).

The pairs (Spec(A), $\tilde{A}$) are the objects in the category of affine schemes, whose morphisms we now discuss.

To describe the morphisms in the category of affine schemes, let (Spec(A), $\tilde{A}$), (Spec(B), $\tilde{B}$) be two objects in the category. Let $\varphi: A \to B$ be a ring homomorphism. Over Spec(A) we define the sheaf of rings $\varphi_*(\tilde{B})$, given by $\varphi_*(\tilde{B})(D(t)) = B_{\varphi(t)} = \tilde{B}(D(\varphi(t)))$, $t \in A$. Then the function $\varphi^a: \mathrm{Spec}(B) \to \mathrm{Spec}(A)$ given by $\varphi^a(\mathfrak{p}) = \varphi^{-1}(\mathfrak{p})$ is continuous, as is seen from the formula $(\varphi^a)^{-1}(D(t)) = D(\varphi(t))$.

Furthermore define $\tilde{\varphi}: \tilde{A} \to \varphi_*(\tilde{B})$ by defining $\tilde{\varphi}(D(t)): A_t \to B_{\varphi(t)}$ as follows: $a/t^n \rightsquigarrow \varphi(a)/\varphi(t^n)$.

To the ring homomorphism φ we have associated a pair of functions $(\varphi^a, \tilde{\varphi})$. Such pairs are precisely the morphisms in the category of affine schemes.

Our dictionary is now adequate, since in fact one can prove that the category of affine schemes is the dual (in the categorical sense) of the category of rings.

APPENDIX

Let $\mathbb{C}$ be the field of complex numbers, $R = \mathbb{C}[X_1, \ldots, X_n]$, $\mathfrak{a}$ an ideal of R such that $\mathfrak{a} = \sqrt{\mathfrak{a}}$. Define $V(\mathfrak{a})$ as follows

$V(\mathfrak{a}) = \{(x_1, \ldots, x_n) \in \mathbb{C}^n \mid f(x_1, \ldots, x_n) = 0 \text{ for all } f \in \mathfrak{a}\}$.

This is the classical notion of an affine variety (in fact, to be strictly classical one should take $\mathfrak{a}$ to be a prime ideal), and it is well known that the points of $V(\mathfrak{a})$ are in a 1-1, onto correspondence with the maximal ideals of the ring $A = R/\mathfrak{a}$. So the classical notion of an affine variety corresponds simply to the set of closed points of Spec(A). In defining Spec(A) as we have, we have in fact added to the classical notion of point a lot of other "undrawable" points, namely the prime ideals of A which are not maximal. We can ask:

a) What are the advantages of such addition?

b) If such addition is indeed advantageous, how could classical geometers get along without it?

The answer to b) is simple: $R/\mathfrak{a}$ is a Jacobson ring, and the knowledge of its maximal ideals determine its prime ideals.

To answer a), at the moment, we make the following four observations:

1) We are not limited to rings of the form $R/\mathfrak{a}$, and, were it so, $\mathfrak{a}$ can be arbitrary, whence $R/\mathfrak{a}$ may have zero divisors (Serre's point of view) and, more strikingly, nilpotent elements.

2) Prime ideals have a "good" functorial behavior (e.g.,the inverse image of a prime ideal under a ring homomorphism is again prime), while maximal ideals do not.

3) The notion of a "ringed space", i.e. a topological space X and a sheaf of rings over X, is the natural tool to give an intrinsic geometric definition of projective varieties (which are definitively not affine).

4) The possibility that $R/\mathfrak{a}$ have nilpotent elements has brought the solutions of long standing conjectures, unsolved until now.

There is one notion that seems to be lost in the transition from the classical case to Spec(A). In the classical case an element of A identifies a regular function over $V(\mathfrak{a})$, with a well defined value $f(x) \in \mathbb{C}$, at each $x \in V(\mathfrak{a})$. Can an element $f \in A$ be considered as a function over Spec(A)? Most definitely, but the value field may change with the point $\mathfrak{p} \in \mathrm{Spec}(A)$. More precisely, $A_{\mathfrak{p}} / \mathfrak{p} A_{\mathfrak{p}}$ is a field, which we denote by $k(\mathfrak{p})$, and we define <u>the value of f at $\mathfrak{p}$</u> as the image of f/1 under the canonical morphism $A_{\mathfrak{p}} \to A_{\mathfrak{p}}/\mathfrak{p}A_{\mathfrak{p}}$. It is trivial to see that, when $A = R/\mathfrak{a}$, and $\mathfrak{p}$ is a maximal ideal of A, then $k(\mathfrak{p}) = \mathbb{C}$, which throws a better light on the classical situation. We point out that, if $f \in A$ is nilpotent, we have the highly non-classical situation of getting $f(\mathfrak{p}) = 0$ for all $\mathfrak{p} \in \mathrm{Spec}(A)$, but $f \neq 0$.

INTRODUCTION

The content of these lectures will be the study of some of the most significant properties (from a geometrical point of view) of local rings. We are limiting ourselves to local rings because, as it appears from the prerequisites, we shall be able to describe and discuss most of their properties without any need for the notion of abstract scheme, which is considerably more general and deeper reaching than the notion of Spec(A).

First a bit of notations. When x denotes a point of Spec(A), by definition x is a prime ideal of A. However, to distinguish the instances when we are looking at x <u>as a point of Spec(A)</u> from when we are looking at x <u>as a prime ideal of A</u>, we write in the latter case j_x for x. Thus the stalk of $\tilde{A}$ over x is written A_{j_x}. We also will write, say, (X, O_X) instead of $(\mathrm{Spec}(A), \tilde{A})$, and then the stalk of O_X over $x \in X$ will be written as $O_{X,x}$.

Let (X, O_X) be an affine scheme, i.e. $(X, O_X) = (\mathrm{Spec}(A), \tilde{A})$ for some ring A. Why do we call the rings $O_{X,x}$ "local"? From classical topological knowledge one would like to say that, in $O_{X,x}$, there is information available about the nature of the neighborhoods of x. This is, in a sense, true, but must be taken with a grain of salt. More specifically, we have $O_{X,x} = \tilde{A}_x = A_{j_x} = \lim_{t \notin j_x} A_t$, and $A_t = \tilde{A}(D(t)) = \Gamma(D(t), O_X)$. Here we have written lim for "direct limit" and $\Gamma(D(t), O_X)$ for the sections of O_X over D(t). Hence $O_{X,x}$ gives us as much information about the neighborhoods of x (the D(t)'s), as a direct limit can give about its "preimages". For $t \notin j_x$ we have canonical homomorphisms $A_t \to A_{j_x}$, hence canonical morphisms (in the category of affine schemes)

$$(\mathrm{Spec}(A_{j_x}), A_{j_x}) \to (\mathrm{Spec}(A_t), A_t) = (D(t), O_x|D(t)).$$

Hence, keeping in mind the duality (in the categorical sense) of the category of affine schemes and the category of rings, we have

$$(\mathrm{Spec}(A_{j_x}), A_{j_x}) \simeq \varprojlim (D(t), O_X|D(t))$$

and the member on the right is $\bigcap_{t \notin j_x} D(t)$. In this case, however, $\bigcap_{t \notin j_x} D(t) \neq x$, in fact equals $\overline{x}$.

So, while the term local is somewhat justified, it is definitely <u>not</u> to be understood to mean "a property holding in the local ring of a point x holds in a neighborhood of x".

What is more likely to happen is the following: we have a morphism $(\varphi, \tilde{\varphi}):(X, O_X) \to (Y, O_Y)$ of affine schemes. A certain property holds both for $O_{X,x}$ and $O_{Y,\varphi(x)}$. Then there exists a neighborhood V of x such that the property holds both for $O_{X,x'}$ and $O_{Y,\varphi(x')}$, if x' ranges over V.

What is, then, the information available in the space $\mathrm{Spec}(A_{j_x})$? Let us look at some examples. Recall, first of all, that the prime ideals of A_{j_x} are in a 1-1, onto correspondence with the prime ideals of A contained in j_x. Hence, as a set, $\mathrm{Spec}(A_{j_x})$ is in a 1-1, onto correspondence with the irreducible closed subsets of Spec(A) containing x.

1) Spec(k), where k is a field, is quite simple. It consists of one point.

2) A_{j_x} is a discrete valuation ring. Here $\mathrm{Spec}(A_{j_x})$ consists of two points, one of which, x, (the maximal ideal) is closed, and the other (the (0) ideal) is open and generic .

3) $A = \mathbb{C}[X, Y]$, $j_x = XA + YA$. Here $\mathrm{Spec}(A_{j_x})$ has (0) as generic point, $j_x \cdot A_{j_x}$ as closed point, and all other points are given by prime ideals of the form $f(X, Y).A_{j_x}$, where $f(X, Y)$ is an irreducible element of A such that $f(0, 0) = 0$.

Let $R = \mathbb{C}[X, Y]$ and consider the following three cases.

1) $A = R/(Y^2 - X^3 - X^2)\cdot R$; $j_x = \overline{X}\cdot A + \overline{Y}A$
(Here $\overline{X}$, $\overline{Y}$ denote the images of X, Y, under the canonical morphism $R \to A$.)

2) $A = R/(Y^2 - X^3)\cdot R$; $j_x = \overline{X}A + \overline{Y}A$.

3) $A = R/(X - Y)R$; $j_x = \overline{X}A + \overline{Y}A$.

The "geometrical" picture of Spec(A) in these cases are as follows (here only one point of Spec(A) is "undrawable", i.e. prime but not maximal: the generic point (0)):

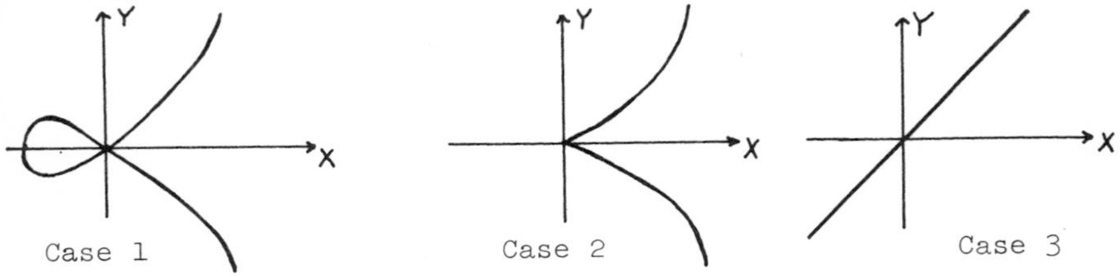

In all three cases the ideal j_x is maximal in A and is represented by the origin in the figures. Now, geometric intuition tells us that, with respect to Spec(A), the origin has different properties in each case. However $\mathrm{Spec}(A_{j_x})$ is the same in all three cases i.e. consists of two points, with one open, generic point, and the other closed. To differentiate the three cases one must hence look at the inner properties of local rings, it is just not sufficient to look at the space $\mathrm{Spec}(A_{j_x})$.

In the category of rings, local rings from a subcategory. However, were one to take this point of view, one would get a lot more morphisms between local rings than one desires.

Let us consider what happens when we have a homomorphism $\varphi : A \to B$ of arbitrary (i.e. not necessarily local) rings. If $\mathfrak{q} \in \mathrm{Spec}(B)$ and $\mathfrak{p} = \varphi^{-1}(\mathfrak{q})$, we have canonically a morphism $\tilde{\varphi} : A_{\mathfrak{p}} \to B_{\mathfrak{q}}$ given by $a/s \rightsquigarrow \varphi(a)/\varphi(s)$. However $\tilde{\varphi}$ has an additional property: $\tilde{\varphi}^{-1}(\mathfrak{q} \cdot B_{\mathfrak{q}}) = \mathfrak{p} A_{\mathfrak{p}}$.

This is the property one wants to have for morphisms of local rings. In short:

The category of local rings and local morphisms is described by:

i) The objects are local rings.

ii) The morphisms are local morphisms, i.e. the inverse image under $A \to B$ of the unique maximal ideal of B is the unique maximal of A.

E.g. The injection of a local ring with no zero divisors into its field of fractions is <u>not</u> a local morphism.

The category of local rings is not a very good one. E.g. it lacks products, it is not closed under finite extensions (i.e. a finite extension of a local ring is not a local ring in general. It is in fact a semi-local ring), and, if $\mathfrak{m}$ denotes the unique maximal ideal of A, Spec(A) - $\mathfrak{m}$ is a scheme, but not affine (that it is a prescheme is seen by Spec(A) - $\mathfrak{m}$ = $\bigcup_{t \in \mathfrak{m}} D(t)$).

We shall hence study the inner properties of local rings A. More specifically, we shall study:

1) Dimension theory. (Dimension, Depth, Regularity)
2) Behavior under local morphisms (Flatness, Ascent, and Descent)
3) Operations on a local ring (Completion, Normalization, Henselization)
4) Stability under the operations in 3. (Excellent rings)

Most of the topics covered will be found, under different treatments, in M. Nagata's book "Local Rings", or J.P. Serre's Algébre locale, Multiplicités, Springer-Verlag, 1965, or E.G.A., IV.

We again remind the reader that we shall limit ourselves to noetherian rings.

§1. DIMENSION THEORY - GENERAL NOTIONS

Let A be a ring. The prime ideals $(\mathfrak{p}_0, \mathfrak{p}_1, \ldots, \mathfrak{p}_n)$ of A are said to form a chain of length n if $\mathfrak{p}_0 \subsetneq \mathfrak{p}_1 \subsetneq \cdots \subsetneq \mathfrak{p}_n$.

Definition 1.1. (Krull) The dimension of A, dim(A) is equal to the l.u.b. of the lengths of the chains of prime ideals in A.

Clearly dim(A) need not be finite. For example, if

$A = k[X_1, X_2, \ldots, X_n \ldots]$ there are clearly chains of arbitrary length.

In fact, even when A is noetherian, an example of Nagata shows that dim(A) need not be finite. It is, however, if A is a local ring. (See theorem 2.3 ahead)

Definition 1.2. Let $\mathfrak{p} \in \mathrm{Spec}(A)$. Then we define

$\dim V(\mathfrak{p}) = \dim(A/\mathfrak{p})$

$\mathrm{Codim}\, V(\mathfrak{p}) = \dim(A_{\mathfrak{p}})$

Proposition 1.1. a) $\dim V(\mathfrak{p}) \leq \dim(A)$; b) $\mathrm{Codim}\, V(\mathfrak{p}) \leq \dim(A)$; c) $\dim V(\mathfrak{p}) + \mathrm{Codim}\, V(\mathfrak{p}) \leq \dim(A)$.

Proof: We have two canonical morphisms

$$A \to A/\mathfrak{p} \; ; \; A \to A_{\mathfrak{p}}$$

and we immediately get a) from the first, b) from the second. Note that a) and b) hold also when the left-hand sides are ∞. Hence c) holds if either of the summands on the left is ∞. Now, any chain in $A/\mathfrak{p}$ gives rise to a chain of equal length in A, of prime ideals containing $\mathfrak{p}$, and any chain in $A_{\mathfrak{p}}$ gives rise to a chain of equal length in A, of prime ideals contained in $\mathfrak{p}$.

Furthermore, we may assume that the chain in $A/\mathfrak{p}$ of length $\dim(A/\mathfrak{p})$ start with (0), and the ones in $A_{\mathfrak{p}}$ of length $\dim(A_{\mathfrak{p}})$ ends with $\mathfrak{p}A_{\mathfrak{p}}$. Hence the corresponding combined chain in A consists of $(\dim V(\mathfrak{p}) + \mathrm{Codim}\, V(\mathfrak{p}) + 1)$ distinct prime ideals, which proves c).

Equally simple is the proof of the following two statements, proof which we leave to the reader.

1) If $\mathfrak{a}$ is any ideal of A, $\dim(A/\mathfrak{a}) \leq \dim(A)$.

2) If $\mathfrak{a}$ is not contained in any minimal prime ideal of A, then $\dim(A/\mathfrak{a}) < \dim(A)$.

Let $\mathfrak{p}, \mathfrak{q} \in \mathrm{Spec}(A)$, $\mathfrak{p} \subset \mathfrak{q}$. A chain $\mathfrak{p} \underset{\neq}{\subset} \mathfrak{p}_1 \underset{\neq}{\subset} \cdots \underset{\neq}{\subset} \mathfrak{q}$ is called a saturated chain connecting $\mathfrak{p}$ and $\mathfrak{q}$ if its length cannot be increased by insertion of some prime ideals.

Definition 1.3. If, for all pairs $\mathfrak{p}, \mathfrak{q} \in \mathrm{Spec}(A)$, all saturated chains connecting $\mathfrak{p}$ and $\mathfrak{q}$ have the same length, A is said to be a catenary ring.

An example of Nagata shows that noetherian local rings need not be catenary.

Proposition 1.2. Let A be an integral local ring. Then

i) If A is catenary for all $\mathfrak{p} \in \mathrm{Spec}(A)$, $\dim(A) = \dim(A_{\mathfrak{p}}) + \dim(A/\mathfrak{p})$.

ii) A is catenary if, and only if, for all $\mathfrak{p}, \mathfrak{q} \in \mathrm{Spec}(A)$ with $\mathfrak{p} \subset \mathfrak{q}$, $\dim A_{\mathfrak{q}} = \dim A_{\mathfrak{p}} + \dim(A_{\mathfrak{q}}/\mathfrak{p}A_{\mathfrak{q}})$.

Proof. i) Since A is an integral local ring, the following statements hold:

a) $A/\mathfrak{p}$, $A_{\mathfrak{p}}$ are integral local rings, hence all dimensions involved are finite.

b) Any chain in A of length equal to dim(A) is a saturated chain connecting (o) and $\mathfrak{m}_A$ ($\mathfrak{m}_A$ denotes the unique maximal ideal of A).

c) Statement b) above holds for $A_{\mathfrak{p}}$ and $A/\mathfrak{p}$. Note that

$$\mathfrak{m}_{A_{\mathfrak{p}}} = \mathfrak{p}A_{\mathfrak{p}} \quad \text{and} \quad \mathfrak{m}_{A/\mathfrak{p}} = \mathfrak{m}_A(A/\mathfrak{p}).$$

Statement i) now follows immediately from a), b), c) above.

ii) We begin by observing that, if A is an arbitrary catenary ring, and $\mathfrak{p} \in \mathrm{Spec}(A)$, then $A_{\mathfrak{p}}$ and $A/\mathfrak{p}$ are catenary. This is easily seen from the 1-1 onto correspondences that exist between the prime ideals of $A_{\mathfrak{p}}$ and $A/\mathfrak{p}$ respectively, and the appropriate prime ideals of A.

Let now $\mathfrak{p}, \mathfrak{q} \in \mathrm{Spec}(A)$, $\mathfrak{p} \subset \mathfrak{q}$ and A an integral, local, catenary ring. Then $A_{\mathfrak{q}}$ is a local, integral catenary ring, and we may apply i) to the ideal $\mathfrak{p}A_{\mathfrak{q}}$. So

$$\dim(A_{\mathfrak{q}}) = \dim(A_{\mathfrak{q}}/\mathfrak{p}A_{\mathfrak{q}}) + \dim((A_{\mathfrak{q}})_{\mathfrak{p}A_{\mathfrak{q}}}).$$

The morphism $\varphi:(A_{\mathfrak{q}})_{\mathfrak{p}A_{\mathfrak{q}}} \to A_{\mathfrak{p}}$ given by $\varphi((a/s)/(b/t)) = at/bs$, $a \in A$, $s,t \notin \mathfrak{q}$, $b \notin \mathfrak{p}$ is well defined ($bs \notin \mathfrak{p}$) and easily seen to be an isomorphism. One part of ii) is proved.

To prove the converse, we observe first that any saturated chain, in A, connecting $\mathfrak{p}$ and $\mathfrak{q}$ gives rise to a saturated chain of equal length in $A_{\mathfrak{q}}/\mathfrak{p}A_{\mathfrak{q}}$ connecting (0) and $\mathfrak{q}A_{\mathfrak{q}}/\mathfrak{p}A_{\mathfrak{q}}$. Hence the length s of any saturated chain in A connecting $\mathfrak{p}$ and $\mathfrak{q}$ is at most $r = \dim(A_{\mathfrak{q}}/\mathfrak{p}A_{\mathfrak{q}})$. We assert $s = r$. When $r = 0, 1$ the assertion is trivially true, and we proceed by induction on r. Let

$$\mathfrak{p} \underset{\neq}{\subset} \mathfrak{p}_1 \underset{\neq}{\subset} \cdots\cdots \underset{\neq}{\subset} \mathfrak{p}_{s-1} \underset{\neq}{\subset} \mathfrak{q}$$

be a saturated chain of length s in A connecting $\mathfrak{p}$ and $\mathfrak{q}$.

We have $\dim(A_{\mathfrak{q}} / \mathfrak{p}_{s-1} A_{\mathfrak{q}}) = 1$. Now

$$\dim(A_{\mathfrak{p}_{s-1}} / \mathfrak{p} A_{\mathfrak{p}_{s-1}}) = \dim(A_{\mathfrak{p}_{s-1}}) - \dim(A_{\mathfrak{p}}) =$$

$$\dim(A_{\mathfrak{q}}) - \dim(A_{\mathfrak{q}} / \mathfrak{p}_{s-1} A_{\mathfrak{q}}) - \dim(A_{\mathfrak{p}}) =$$

$$\dim(A_{\mathfrak{q}} / \mathfrak{p} A_{\mathfrak{q}}) - 1 = r - 1.$$

By induction $s - 1 = r - 1$ and we are done.

If $\varphi: A \to B$ is a homomorphism, B can be considered as an A-algebra by $a \cdot b = \varphi(a) \cdot b$. We say that <u>B is integral over A</u> if every $b \in B$ satisfies an equation of integral dependence over A, i.e. $b^n + a_{n-1} b^{n-1} + \ldots + a_0 = 0$, $a_i \in A$, $n > 0$.

<u>Theorem 1.1</u>. (Going-up theorem). Let $\varphi: A \to B$ be a homomorphism, B integral over A. Then

i) $\dim(B) \leqq \dim(A)$ (lame going-up theorem).

ii) If φ is mono, $\dim(A) = \dim(B)$.

<u>Proof</u>: i) Let $\mathfrak{q}$ be a proper prime ideal of B. We assert:

a) $\varphi^{-1}(\mathfrak{q}) \neq A$

b) $\varphi^{-1}(\mathfrak{q}) \neq \ker(\varphi)$ if $\mathfrak{q} \neq (0)$,

and B is an integral domain. a) is trivial, since $\varphi(1) = 1$ and $\mathfrak{q}$ is proper.

To prove b) assume $\varphi^{-1}(\mathfrak{q}) = \ker \varphi$. Then $\operatorname{Im} A \cap \mathfrak{q} = (0)$. Let $b \in \mathfrak{q}$, $b \neq 0$. Let

$$b^n + c_{n-1} b^{n-1} + \ldots + c_0 = 0$$

be an equation of integral dependence of <u>minimal degree</u>. Now $c_0 \in \operatorname{Im}(A)$ and clearly $c_0 \in \mathfrak{q}$. Hence $c_0 = 0$, and

$$b(b^{n-1} + C_{n-1} b^{n-2} + \dots + C_1) = 0.$$

this is a contradiction, since B is an integral domain.

To prove i) from a) and b), let $\mathfrak{p} \subsetneq \mathfrak{q}$ be prime ideals of B. From $A \xrightarrow{\varphi} B \xrightarrow{c} B/\mathfrak{p}$ we see that $B/\mathfrak{p}$ is an integral domain, integral over A, and that

$$\varphi^{-1}(\mathfrak{p}) = \ker(c \circ \varphi)$$

$$\varphi^{-1}(\mathfrak{q}) = (c \circ \varphi)^{-1} (\mathfrak{q} \cdot B/\mathfrak{p}) \text{ and } \mathfrak{q} B/\mathfrak{p} \neq (0).$$

Hence, from b) above $\varphi^{-1}(\mathfrak{q}) \subsetneq \varphi^{-1}(\mathfrak{p})$, and i) follows.

<u>Note</u>: i) holds under the weaker assumption that B is algebraic over A.

ii) Let $\mathfrak{p} \subsetneq \mathfrak{q}$ be prime ideals of A. By theorem 1 of Chapter V, 2 of B.C.A., there exists a prime ideal $\mathfrak{p}'$ in B such that $\varphi^{-1}(\mathfrak{p}') = \mathfrak{p}$. Then $\varphi(\mathfrak{p}) \subset \mathfrak{p}'$, the morphism

$$\varphi' : A/\mathfrak{p} \to B/\mathfrak{p}'$$

is mono, and $B/\mathfrak{p}'$ is integral over $A/\mathfrak{p}$. Now $\mathfrak{q}(A/\mathfrak{p}) \neq (0)$ is a prime ideal of $A/\mathfrak{p}$, and hence there exists a prime ideal $\mathfrak{q}''$ of $B/\mathfrak{p}'$ such that $\varphi'^{-1}(\mathfrak{q}'') = \mathfrak{q}(A/\mathfrak{p})$. We have $\mathfrak{q}'' = \mathfrak{q}' \cdot B/\mathfrak{p}'$, where $\mathfrak{q}'$ is a prime ideal of B, and clearly $\varphi^{-1}(\mathfrak{q}') = \mathfrak{q}$. Since $\mathfrak{q}(A/\mathfrak{p}) \neq (0)$ and φ' is mono, we have $\mathfrak{q}'' \neq (0)$, whence $\mathfrak{q}' \supsetneq \mathfrak{p}'$. This implies

$$\dim(A) \leqq \dim(B) \quad \text{whence ii) follows.}$$

Definition 1.2. gives the notion of dimension for an irreducible closed subset of Spec(A). We extend this notion to arbitrary closed subsets by the formula

$$\dim(V(\mathfrak{a})) = \dim(A/\mathfrak{a})$$

where $\mathfrak{a}$ is an arbitrary ideal of A.

If M is a finitely generated A-module we define

$$\dim(M) = \dim(\mathrm{Supp}(M)) = \dim(A/\mathrm{ann}(M)).$$

Here we use the fact, mentioned in the preliminaries, that Supp(M) is the closure in Spec(A) of Ass(M), and Ass(M) consists of the prime ideals associated to ann(M).

If $N \subset M$ is another A-module we see trivially that

$$\dim(N) \leqq \dim(M)$$

$$\dim(M/_N) \leqq \dim(M)$$

In fact $\mathrm{ann}(N) \supset \mathrm{ann}(M)$, $\mathrm{ann}(M/_N) \supset \mathrm{ann}(M)$.

A non-trivial statement, proved in Bourbaki's, chapter IV, §2, is the following:

<u>Theorem 1.2.</u> $\dim(M) = 0$ if, and only if, M has finite length, in the composition series sense.

§2. HILBERT-SAMUEL POLYNOMIAL

Let H be a graded ring, i.e.

$$H = \bigoplus_{n \geqq 0} H_n$$

where H_n are (additive) groups and $h_n \cdot h_m \in H_{n+m}$, for $h_n \in H_n$, $h_m \in H_m$. Clearly H_n is an H_0-module. We assume:

a) H_0 is an artinian ring

b) H is generated (as an H_0-algebra) by finitely many elements of H_1.

An H-module M is called graded if $M = \bigoplus_n M_n$, where M_n are H_o-modules and

$$H_n M_p \subset M_{n+p}.$$

If M is a finitely generated H-module, then M_n is a finitely generated H_o-module and (since H_o is artinian) M_n has finite length.

Definition 2.1. The Hilbert-Samuel Polynomial of M, $\chi(M, n)$, is given by

$$\chi(M, n) = \text{length}_{H_o} M_n \quad \text{for large } n.$$

Of course one needs to prove that $\chi(M, n)$ is indeed a polynomial. In fact

Theorem 2.1. (Hilbert) Let H, M be as stated above. Then there exists a polynomial $P(X) \in Q[X]$, which achieves integer values for integer values of X and such that, for all sufficiently large n,

$$\chi(M, n) = P(n)$$

Proof: Since H is finitely generated over H_o by H_1, we have a homogeneous epimorphism (of degree 0)

$$H_o[X_1,\ldots,X_r] \xrightarrow{c} H \to 0$$

and M becomes a finitely generated $H_o[X_1,\ldots,X_r]$-module. Now $\text{length}_{H_o} M_n$ is independent of whether we consider M as an H-module or an $H_o[X_1,\ldots,X_r]$-module (since c is onto). Hence we may assume $H = H_o[X_1,\ldots,X_r]$.

We proceed by induction on r. When r = 0, $H = H_o$ and, since

M is finitely generated by, say, $m_i \in M_{n_i}$, we have $M_n = 0$ if $n \geqq \max_i \{n_i\}$. Hence $\chi(M, n) = 0$ for n sufficiently large.

Let $\varphi_r : M \to M$ be given by $\varphi_r(m) = X_r \cdot m$. Then φ_r is a homogeneous morphism of degree 1 and we have

$$0 \to N \to M \xrightarrow{\varphi_r} M \to C \to 0$$

$$0 \to N_n \to M_n \to M_{n+1} \to C_{n+1} \to 0$$

Since $\text{length}_{H_o}(\cdot)$ is an additive function we have

$$\chi(M, n+1) - \chi(M, n) = \chi(C, n+1) - \chi(N, n)$$

For $n \in N$, $c \in C$ we have $X_r \cdot n = 0$, $X_r \cdot c = 0$, hence N and C are $H_o[X_1, \ldots, X_{r-1}]$ modules, and, by induction, $\chi(C, n+1) - \chi(N, n)$ is a rational polynomial in n, for sufficiently large n. A standard argument now shows that $\chi(M, n)$ is also a rational polynomial, for n sufficiently large.

For the remainder of this section we assume that A is a noetherian, semi-local ring.

Definition 2.2. Let $\mathfrak{q}$ be an ideal of A. We say that $\mathfrak{q}$ is an ideal of definition of A, if the ring $A/\mathfrak{q}$ is artinian.

We recall here that a ring A is called artinian if it satisfies the descending chain condition or, equivalently, if every prime ideal of A is maximal.

We assert:

Proposition 2.1. Let $\mathfrak{q}$ be an ideal of A. The following three conditions are equivalent.

a) $\mathfrak{q}$ is an ideal of definition of A

b) $A/\mathfrak{q}$ has finite length (in the composition series sense)

c) $\mathfrak{q} \supset \mathfrak{N}^k$, where $\mathfrak{N}$ denotes the radical of A.

Proof:

b) $\Longrightarrow$ a) is immediate, since $A/\mathfrak{q}$ satisfies both chain conditions. a) $\Longrightarrow$ b) follows from the fact that an artinian ring is also noetherian.

c) $\Longrightarrow$ a) follows from the following observation: if $\mathfrak{q} \supset \mathfrak{N}^k$ and a prime ideal $\mathfrak{p}$ contains $\mathfrak{q}$, then $\mathfrak{p}$ is one of the maximal ideals of A. To see that a) $\Longrightarrow$ c) we observe first, that since $A/\mathfrak{q}$ is artinian, $\mathrm{rad}(A/\mathfrak{q})$ = the set of nilpotents in $A/\mathfrak{q}$. Now, clearly, $\mathrm{rad}(A/\mathfrak{q}) = \varphi(\mathfrak{N})$, where $\varphi: A \to A/\mathfrak{q}$ is the canonical epimorphism.

If $\mathfrak{q}$ is an ideal of definition of A and M is a finitely generated A-module, $M/\mathfrak{q}M$ is a finitely generated $A/\mathfrak{q}$-module (in fact $M/\mathfrak{q}M \simeq M \otimes_A A/\mathfrak{q}$), hence $M/\mathfrak{q}M$ has finite length.

Theorem 2.2. (Hilbert-Samuel) Let A, $\mathfrak{q}$, M be as above. Then

a) $M/\mathfrak{q}^n M$ has finite length

b) $\mathrm{length}_A(M/\mathfrak{q}^n M) = P_{\mathfrak{q}}(M, n)$ is a polynomial in n for n sufficiently large.

Proof: We prove a) by induction on n. When n = 1 the assertion is precisely the observation we made previous to the statement of the theorem. Clearly, for all k, $\mathfrak{q}^k/\mathfrak{q}^{k+1}$ is a finitely generated A-module (A noetherian). Hence $(M/\mathfrak{q}M) \otimes_A \mathfrak{q}^k/\mathfrak{q}^{k+1}$ is a finitely generated A-module. The epimorphism

$$(M/\mathfrak{q}M) \otimes \mathfrak{q}^k/\mathfrak{q}^{k+1} \to \mathfrak{q}^k M/\mathfrak{q}^{k+1} M$$

given by $\overline{m} \otimes \overline{q} \rightsquigarrow \overline{qm}$ (here $\overline{m}$, $\overline{q}$ denote the equivalence classes of $m \in M$, $q \in \mathfrak{q}^k$) shows that $\mathfrak{q}^k M/\mathfrak{q}^{k+1} M$ is a finitely generated A-module. Finally the exact sequence

$$(\ast)\quad 0 \to \mathfrak{q}^n M/\mathfrak{q}^{n+1} M \to M/\mathfrak{q}^{n+1} M \to M/\mathfrak{q}^n M \to 0$$

and the induction assumption prove a).

To prove b) we define

$$H = \operatorname{gr}_{\mathfrak{q}}(A) = \bigoplus_{i \geqq 0} (\mathfrak{q}^i/\mathfrak{q}^{i+1})$$

$$M' = \operatorname{gr}(M) = \bigoplus_{i \geqq 0} (\mathfrak{q}^i M/\mathfrak{q}^{i+1} M)$$

where $\mathfrak{q}^0 = A$. Since $H_0 = A/\mathfrak{q}$ is artinian, H is generated over H_0 by finitely many elements of $H_1 = \mathfrak{q}/\mathfrak{q}^2$ (any A-basis of $\mathfrak{q}$ will do) and M' is a finitely generated H-module (any A-basis of M will do); we can apply Theorem 2.1 and get

$$\operatorname{length}(\mathfrak{q}^n M/\mathfrak{q}^{n+1} M) = \text{a polynomial in } n \text{ for } n \gg 0.$$

(We write $n \gg 0$ for "...n sufficiently large".)

From the above exact sequence ($\ast$) we get

$$\operatorname{length}(M/\mathfrak{q}^{n+1} M) - \operatorname{length}(M/\mathfrak{q}^n M) = \operatorname{length}(\mathfrak{q}^n M/\mathfrak{q}^{n+1} M)$$

or

$$P_{\mathfrak{q}}(M, n+1) - P_{\mathfrak{q}}(M, n) = \text{a polynomial in } n \text{ for } n \gg 0.$$

The theorem is proved.

<u>Note</u>: The geometrical significance of the polynomial $P_{\mathfrak{q}}(M, n)$ was discovered by Serre, and it is the following. Let H, M' be as in the proof of the theorem. Let X = Proj(H), $\mathcal{M}$ = the sheaf over Proj(H) associated to the graded module M': then <u>for every n</u>, $P_{\mathfrak{q}}(M', n) = \sum_i (-1)^i \operatorname{length} H^i(X, \mathcal{M}(n))$.

We do not go into further details, except to point out that, for $n >> 0$ $H^i(X, \mathcal{J}(n)) = 0$, which throws a better light on the somewhat unsatisfactory statement of b), (for $n >> 0$).

Let now A, $\mathfrak{q}$, M be as usual. A filtration $M = M_o \supset M_1 \supset \ldots \supset M_n \supset \ldots$ is called a $\mathfrak{q}$ - good filtration of M if $\mathfrak{q} M_n \subset M_{n+1}$, with equality holding for $n \geqq n_o$.

We assert

Proposition 2.2. Under the above hypotheses, for $n >> 0$ $\text{length}_A(M/M_n) = P((M_n), n)$ = a polynomial in n of degree and coefficient of the term of highest degree equaling those of $P_{\mathfrak{q}}(M, n)$.

Proof: As in the proof of theorem, we prove by induction on n that M/M_n has finite length. In fact M/M_1 is an $A/\mathfrak{q}$ - module finitely generated, and

$$0 \to M_n/M_{n+1} \to M/M_{n+1} \to M/M_n \to 0$$

and $\mathfrak{q}(M_n/M_{n+1}) = 0$, whence M_n/M_{n+1} is an $A/\mathfrak{q}$ -module and has finite length.

Consider now the module M_{n_o}. It is a finitely generated A-module and $M_{n+n_o} = \mathfrak{q}^n M_{n_o}$. Hence, by theorem 2.2

$$\text{length}(M_{n_o}/M_{n+n_o}) = \text{a polynomial in } n, \text{ for } n >> 0.$$

The exact sequence

$$0 \to M_{n_o}/M_{n+n_o} \to M/M_{n+n_o} \to M/M_{n_o} \to 0$$

shows that $\text{length}(M/M_n)$ is a polynomial in n for $n >> 0$. The inclusions

$$\mathfrak{q}^{n+n_o} M \subset M_{n+n_o} \subset \mathfrak{q}^{n} M \subset M_n$$

give exact sequences

$$0 \to M_{n+n_o}/\mathfrak{q}^{n+n_o} M \to M/\mathfrak{q}^{n+n_o} M \to M/M_{n+n_o} \to 0$$

$$0 \to \mathfrak{q}^n M/M_{n+n_o} \to M/M_{n+n_o} \to M/\mathfrak{q}^n M \to 0$$

$$0 \to M_n/\mathfrak{q}^n M \to M/\mathfrak{q}^n M \to M/M_n \to 0$$

whence

$$P_{\mathfrak{q}}(M, n+n_o) \geqq P((M_{n+n_o}), n+n_o) \geqq P_{\mathfrak{q}}(M, n) \geqq P((M_n), n).$$

Since $P_{\mathfrak{q}}$ and P are polynomials, they must have the same degree and the same highest degree coefficient, Q.E.D.

Proposition 2.3. Let $\mathfrak{q}$, $\mathfrak{q}'$ be ideals of definition of A, M a finitely generated A-module. Then $P_{\mathfrak{q}}$, $P_{\mathfrak{q}'}$ are polynomials of the same degree.

Proof: Since $\mathrm{rad}(\mathfrak{q}') = \mathrm{rad}(\mathfrak{q}) = \mathfrak{m}$ we have (A is noetherian) $\mathfrak{q} \supset \mathfrak{q}'^p$ and $\mathfrak{q}' \supset \mathfrak{q}^m$, for some m. Hence

$$0 \to \mathfrak{q}'^n M/\mathfrak{q}^{nm} M \to M/\mathfrak{q}^{nm} M \to M/\mathfrak{q}'^n M \to 0$$

whence $P_{\mathfrak{q}'}(M, n) \leqq P_{\mathfrak{q}}(M, mn)$ and similarly

$$P_{\mathfrak{q}}(M, n) \leqq P_{\mathfrak{q}'}(M, pn)$$

and the proposition is proved.

Definition 2.3. Let A, M be given as above. Then deg $P_{\mathfrak{q}}$

(which, by the proposition above is independent of $\mathfrak{q}$) is denoted by d(M).

Proposition 2.4. Let A be as usual, and let

$$0 \to M' \to M \to M'' \to 0$$

be an exact sequence of finitely generated A-modules. Then, for any ideal $\mathfrak{q}$ of definition of A:

$$\deg[P_{\mathfrak{q}}(M) - P_{\mathfrak{q}}(M') - P_{\mathfrak{q}}(M'')] \leqq d(M') - 1 \leqq d(M) - 1$$

Proof: By the Artin-Rees lemma (B.C.A., III, 3, corollary 1) the submodules $M'_n = \mathfrak{q}^n M \cap M$ of M' form a $\mathfrak{q}$- good filtration of M'. By proposition 2.2 we have (*) $P_{\mathfrak{q}}(M')$ and $P(M'_n)$ have the same degree and the same highest degree coefficient.
The exact sequence

$$0 \to \mathfrak{q}^n M \cap M' \to \mathfrak{q}^n M \to \mathfrak{q}^n M'' \to 0$$

gives an exact sequence

$$0 \to M'/\mathfrak{q}^n M \cap M' \to M/\mathfrak{q}^n M \to M''/\mathfrak{q}^n M'' \to 0$$

whence

$$P_{\mathfrak{q}}(M, n) - P_{\mathfrak{q}}(M'', n) - P(M'_n, n) = 0$$

or

$$P_{\mathfrak{q}}(M) - P_{\mathfrak{q}}(M'') - P(M'_n) = 0$$

Hence

$$P(M'_n) = P_{\mathfrak{q}}(M) - P_{\mathfrak{q}}(M'')$$

and, by (*),

$$P_{\mathfrak{q}}(M') = P_{\mathfrak{q}}(M) - P_{\mathfrak{q}}(M'') + \text{a polyn. of degree}$$

at most $d(M') - 1$.

The first inequality is proved. The second follows immediately from observing that $0 \leqq P_{\mathfrak{q}}(M'', n) \leqq P_{\mathfrak{q}}(M, n)$, for $n \gg 0$, whence

$$\deg P_{\mathfrak{q}}(M'') \leqq \deg P_{\mathfrak{q}}(M).$$

Let M be a finitely generated A-module, and let $y_1, \ldots, y_k \in \mathfrak{r}$ be a set of generators of $\mathfrak{r}$. Then $M/y_1 M + \ldots + y_k M$ is an $A/\mathfrak{r}$-module and hence has finite length. With this in mind we give the following:

Definition 2.4. We denote by $s(M)$ the smallest integer k satisfying the following condition:

there exist k elements $x_1, \ldots, x_k$ in $\mathfrak{r}$ such that

$$M/x_1 M + \ldots + x_k M \text{ has finite length}$$

We are now in the position of proving the main result of dimension theory, namely

Theorem 2.3. (Krull-Chevalley-Samuel) Let A be a semi-local noetherian ring, M a finitely generated A-module. Then $\dim(M) = d(M) = s(M)$.

Proof: (Serre). We shall prove

1) $\dim(M) \leqq d(M)$

2) $d(M) \leqq s(M)$

3) $s(M) \leqq \dim(M)$.

We start with the following

Lemma 2.1. Let $x \in \mathcal{N}$, consider the exact sequence

$$0 \to {}_xM \to M \xrightarrow{\varphi} M \to M/xM \to 0$$

where $\varphi(m) = xm$. Then

i) $s(M) \leqq s(M/xM) + 1$

ii) Let $(\mathfrak{p}_1, \ldots, \mathfrak{p}_m)$ denote those points of Supp(M) such that $\dim(A/\mathfrak{p}_i) = \dim(M)$, $i = 1, \ldots, m$. If $x \notin \bigcup_{i=1}^{m} \mathfrak{p}_i$ then $\dim(M/xM) \leqq \dim(M) - 1$

iii) $\deg[P_{\mathfrak{q}}({}_xM) - P_{\mathfrak{q}}(M/xM)] \leqq d(M) - 1$, where $\mathfrak{q}$ is any ideal of definition of A.

Proof:

i) Let $N = M/xM$, and let $y_1, \ldots, y_k \in \mathcal{N}$ such that $N/y_1 N + \ldots + y_k N$ has finite length and $k = s(N)$. The isomorphism

$$N/y_1 N + \ldots + y_k N \to M/xM + y_1 M + \ldots + y_k M$$

proves i).

ii) We start with a word about the $\mathfrak{p}_i$'s. By definition we have $\dim(M) = \dim(A/_{\mathrm{ann}(M)})$. If $\mathfrak{p}_1, \mathfrak{p}_2, \ldots, \mathfrak{p}_t$, $t \geqq m$, denote the prime ideals associated to ann(M) in A one easily sees that

$$\dim(M) = \max_{1 \leqq i \leqq t} \dim(A/\mathfrak{p}_i).$$

Hence the prime ideals mentioned in the statement of ii) are to be found among the points of Ass(M).

We have to compare $\dim(A/\mathrm{ann}(M/xM))$ with $\dim(A/\mathrm{ann}\, M)$ Let $\mathfrak{q}_1, \dots, \mathfrak{q}_t$ be those prime ideals in A associated to $\mathrm{ann}(M/xM)$ and such that $\dim(M/xM) = \dim(A/\mathfrak{q}_j)$. Then, for some i_j, $1 \leqq i_j \leqq t$, we have $\mathfrak{q}_j \supset \mathfrak{p}_{i_j}$. Let $\mathfrak{q}'_0 \underset{\neq}{\subset} \mathfrak{q}'_1 \underset{\neq}{\subset} \dots \underset{\neq}{\subset} \mathfrak{q}'_k$ be a chain of prime ideals of maximal length in $A/\mathrm{ann}(M/xM)$, i.e. $k = \dim(M/xM)$. The prime ideal $\mathfrak{q}'_0$ corresponds to a prime ideal $\mathfrak{q}$ of A containing $\mathrm{ann}(M/xM)$ and, from $k = \dim(M/xM)$ one sees that $\mathfrak{q} = \mathfrak{q}_j$ for some j. We proceed in steps.

<u>Case 1</u>. $\mathfrak{q}_j \supset \mathfrak{p}_{i_j}$, $i_j > m$. Then

$$\dim(M/xM) = \dim A/\mathfrak{q}_j \leqq \dim A/\mathfrak{p}_{i_j} < \dim(M)$$

and ii) is proved in this case.

<u>Case 2</u>. $\mathfrak{q}_j \supset \mathfrak{p}_{i_j}$, $i_j \leqq m$. Then (since $x \in \mathfrak{q}_j$), $\mathfrak{q}_j \underset{\neq}{\supset} \mathfrak{p}_{i_j}$ and the chain $\mathfrak{p}_{i_j} \underset{\neq}{\subset} \mathfrak{q}_j \underset{\neq}{\subset} \dots$ shows that $\dim(M) \geqq k + 1$ and ii) is proved in this case also.

iii). We have two exact sequences

$$0 \to {}_xM \to M \to xM \to 0$$

$$0 \to xM \to M \to M/xM \to 0$$

Now

$$\deg[P_{\mathfrak{q}}({}_xM) - P_{\mathfrak{q}}(M/xM)] =$$

$$\deg[(P_{\mathfrak{q}}({}_xM) + P_{\mathfrak{q}}(xM) - P_{\mathfrak{q}}(M)) + (P_{\mathfrak{q}}(M) - P_{\mathfrak{q}}(xM) - P_{\mathfrak{q}}(M/xM)]$$

and, by proposition 2.2 the right hand side is the degree of the sum of two polynomials, one of degree $\leqq d({}_xM) - 1 \leqq d(M) - 1$, the other of degree $\leqq d(xM) - 1 \leqq d(M) - 1$. The lemma is proved. Now we return to the proof of the theorem.

1) $\dim(M) \leqq d(M)$. We proceed by induction on $d(M)$. $d(M) = 0$. Then $P_{\mathfrak{q}}(M)$ = constant, whence

$$\text{length } (M/\mathfrak{q}^n M) = \text{length } (M/\mathfrak{q}^{n+1} M) \text{ for } n >> 0.$$

The exact sequence

$$0 \to \mathfrak{q}^n M/\mathfrak{q}^{n+1} M/ \to M/\mathfrak{q}^{n+1} M \to M/\mathfrak{q}^n M \to 0$$

shows length $(\mathfrak{q}^n M/\mathfrak{q}^{n+1} M) = 0$ whence $\mathfrak{q}^n M = \mathfrak{q}^{n+1} M$. Now, we take $\mathfrak{q} = \mathfrak{r}$, and then we have $\bigcap_{n \geqq 0} \mathfrak{r}^n = (0)$, whence $\mathfrak{r}^n M = 0$ for $n >> 0$. Hence M is an $A/\mathfrak{r}^n$-module, and since $A/\mathfrak{r}^n$ is artinian, its dimension is 0, whence $\dim(M) = 0$. Hence 1 holds when $d(M) = 0$.

Choose a prime $\mathfrak{p}_0 \in \text{Ass}(M)$ such that $\dim(M) = \dim(A/\mathfrak{p}_0)$. Since $\mathfrak{p}_0$ is <u>the annihilator</u> of an element $m \in M$, the submodule $N = Am \subset M$ is isomorphic to $A/\mathfrak{p}_0$. By proposition 2.4 we have

$$d(N) \leqq d(M)$$

and

$$\dim(N) = \dim(M)$$

Hence it suffices to prove 1) for N. Let $\mathfrak{p}_0 \underset{\neq}{\subset} \mathfrak{p}_1 \underset{\neq}{\subset} \mathfrak{p}_2 \cdots \underset{\neq}{\subset} \mathfrak{p}_n$ be a chain of maximal length in A, corresponding to a chain of maximal length in $A/\mathfrak{p}_0$ (note that $n = +\infty$ is a priori possible). If $\mathfrak{p}_1 \cap \mathfrak{r} \subset \mathfrak{p}_0$, then $\mathfrak{p}_0 \supset \mathfrak{r}$, whence is maximal (because A is semi-local), a contradiction.

Choose $x \in \mathfrak{p}_1 \cap \mathfrak{m}$, $x \notin \mathfrak{p}_0$.
We have

$$N/xN = (A/xA) \otimes_A N$$

and, from proposition 18 of B.C.A., II, §4 we get

$$\mathrm{Supp}(N/xN) = \mathrm{Supp}(N) \cap V(x).$$

Hence $\mathfrak{p}_1, \mathfrak{p}_2, \ldots, \mathfrak{p}_n \in \mathrm{Supp}(N/xN)$, whence $\dim(N/xN) \geqq n - 1$ (in particular, if $\dim(N/xN)$ is finite, so is n). Now trivially the homomorphism $A/\mathfrak{p}_0 \to A/\mathfrak{p}_0$ given by $\bar{a} \rightsquigarrow x\bar{a}$ is injective, hence ${}_xN = 0$. By lemma 2.1 we get $d(N/xN) \leqq d(N) - 1 \leqq d(M) - 1$, and by induction $\dim(N/xN) \leqq d(N/xN)$ (and we have proved that n is finite). Now

$$\dim(M) = n \leqq \dim(N/xN) + 1 \leqq d(N/xN) + 1 \leqq d(M)$$

and 1) is proved.
We observe here that we have actually shown $\dim(M) < +\infty$.

2) $d(M) \leqq s(M)$. Let $\{x_i\}_{1 \leqq i \leqq n}$ be elements of $\mathfrak{m}$ such that, letting $\mathfrak{a} = x_1 A + \ldots + x_n A$, we have length $(M/\mathfrak{a} M) < +\infty$ and $n = s(M)$. Let $\mathfrak{q} = \mathfrak{a} + \mathfrak{m} \cap \mathrm{ann}(M)$. We have $\mathrm{ann}(M/\mathfrak{q} M) \supset \mathfrak{a}$, hence the prime ideals in $\mathrm{Ass}(M/\mathfrak{q}M)$ are maximal, and therefore $\mathfrak{q} \supset \mathfrak{m}^k$ for some k, i.e. $\mathfrak{q}$ is an ideal of definition of A. Now clearly $\mathfrak{q}^m M = \mathfrak{a}^m M$, whence $\mathfrak{q}^m M/\mathfrak{q}^{m+1} M = \mathfrak{a}^m M/\mathfrak{a}^{m+1} M$. Let $z_1, \ldots, z_r$ be a minimal set of generators of M over A. Then the elements $\{x_1^{\nu_1} \ldots x_n^{\nu_n} \cdot z_i\}$ $1 \leq i \leq r$, $\nu_1 + \ldots + \nu_n = m$ are a set of generators of $\mathfrak{a}^m M/\mathfrak{a}^{m+1} M$ over $A/\mathfrak{q}$. Let length $(A/\mathfrak{q}) =$

a ($a < +\infty$ since $A/\mathfrak{q}$ is artinian). Now

$$\text{length}\,(\mathfrak{q}^m M/\mathfrak{q}^{m+1} M) = \text{length}\,(\mathfrak{a}^m M/\mathfrak{a}^{m+1} M) \leqq$$

$$a.r. \binom{n+m-1}{n-1} = \text{a polyn. in } m \text{ of degree } n-1.$$

The exact sequence

$$0 \to \mathfrak{q}^m M/\mathfrak{q}^{m+1} M \to M/\mathfrak{q}^{m+1} M \to M/\mathfrak{q}^m M \to 0$$

shows 2).

3) $s(M) \leqq \dim(M)$. We proceed by induction on $\dim(M)$ (which is finite by 1).

$\dim(M) = 0$. Then length $(M) < +\infty$ (since $A/\text{ann}\, M$ is artinian) and no elements of $\mathfrak{r}$ are needed to have length $(M/x_1M+\ldots+x_kM) < +\infty$. Hence $s(M) = 0$ and 3) holds. Let $n = \dim(M) \geqq 1$. Let $\{\mathfrak{p}_i\}_{1\leqq i\leqq m}$ be those elements of Ass(M) such that $\dim(M) = \dim(A/\mathfrak{p}_i)$. Since $n \geqq 1$ the $\mathfrak{p}_i$ are not maximal. We assert:

$\mathfrak{r} \not\subset \bigcup_{i=1}^{m} \mathfrak{p}_i$. In fact, if $\mathfrak{r} \subset \bigcup_{i=1}^{m} \mathfrak{p}_i$, then, by proposition 2 of B.C.A., II, §1, we have $\mathfrak{r} \subset \mathfrak{p}_i$ for some i, a contradiction, since $\mathfrak{p}_i$ is not maximal. Hence we can choose $x \in \mathfrak{r}$, $x \notin \bigcup_{i=1}^{m} \mathfrak{p}_i$. By lemma 2.1 we have

$$s(M) \leqq s(M/xM) + 1$$

and $\dim(M/xM) \leqq \dim(M) - 1$. Hence, by induction

$$s(M/xM) \leqq \dim(M/xM)$$

and finally

$$s(M) \leqq s(M/xM) + 1 \leqq \dim(M/xM) + 1 \leqq \dim(M),$$

Q.E.D.

Appendix

We give a brief description of the geometrical meaning of the three numbers dim(M), s(M), d(M).

We admit right off that d(M) is a far-reaching concept leading in particular to certain results of intersection theory, and we shall limit ourselves to a geometrical interpretation of dim(M) and s(M).

dim(M) is the simplest of the two. It simply gives the maximal length of irredundant descending chains of irreducible subsets of Supp(M). (Such chains must necessarily terminate with a closed point.)

s(M) has a somewhat more sophisticated interpretation. Remembering that $\mathrm{Supp}(M/xM) = \mathrm{Supp}(M) \cap V(x)$ and that $\mathrm{length}\ (M) < +\infty \iff \dim(M) = 0 \iff \dim(\mathrm{Supp}(M)) = 0 \iff$ (by above remark) $\iff$ Supp(M) consists of a finite number of closed points. We see that s(M) is the smallest number of "hypersurfaces" (the V(x)'s) such that their intersection with Supp(M) is zero dimensional.

There is a fourth integer that one should introduce in this connection, but which is related to the previous three, in general, by an inequality rather than equality.

Let A be a local ring, $\mathfrak{m}$ its maximal ideal. The A-module $\mathfrak{m}/\mathfrak{m}^2$ is (clearly!) annihilated by $\mathfrak{m}$, hence $\mathfrak{m}/\mathfrak{m}^2$ is an $A/\mathfrak{m}$ module, i.e. a vector space over $k = A/\mathfrak{m}$. $\dim_k(\mathfrak{m}/\mathfrak{m}^2)$ is the fourth integer we wish to consider. We assert:

Proposition 2.5.

$$s(A) \leq \dim_k(\mathfrak{m}/\mathfrak{m}^2).$$

<u>Proof</u>: Let $x_1,\ldots,x_n$ be elements of $\mathfrak{m}$ such that their equivalence classes (mod $\mathfrak{m}^2$) form a basis of $\mathfrak{m}/\mathfrak{m}^2$ over $A/\mathfrak{m}$. We assert that $x_1,\ldots,x_n$ form a system of generators of $\mathfrak{m}$. Let

$$M = x_1 A \oplus x_2 A \oplus \ldots \oplus x_n A$$
$$N = \mathfrak{m}$$

and let $u : M \to N$ be defined by $u(a_1 x_1 \oplus \ldots \oplus a_n x_n) = \sum a_i x_i$. Let $\mathfrak{a} = \mathfrak{m}^2 \subset \mathrm{rad}(A) = \mathfrak{m}$. Now

$$N \otimes A/\mathfrak{m}^2 \simeq \mathfrak{m}/\mathfrak{m}^2$$

and

$$u \otimes \mathrm{id}_{A/\mathfrak{m}^2} : M \otimes A/\mathfrak{m}^2 \to \mathfrak{m}/\mathfrak{m}^2$$

is surjective, since we have the commutative diagram

$$\begin{array}{ccc} M \otimes A/\mathfrak{m} \simeq \bigoplus_{i=1}^{n} k & & \\ \uparrow \varphi & \searrow \Psi & \\ M \otimes A/\mathfrak{m}^2 & \xrightarrow[u \otimes \mathrm{id}_{A/\mathfrak{m}^2}]{} & \mathfrak{m}/\mathfrak{m}^2 \end{array}$$

and φ, Ψ are surjective. By Nakayama's lemma we have that u is surjective, which proves that $x_1,\ldots,x_n$ form a system of generators of $\mathfrak{m}$. Hence $A/x_1 A + \ldots + x_n A = k$ and $\mathrm{length}_A(k) < +\infty$.

Hence $s(A) \leqq n = \mathrm{rank}_k(\mathfrak{m}/\mathfrak{m}^2)$, Q.E.D.

We show with an example that $s(A) < \mathrm{rank}_k(\mathfrak{m}/\mathfrak{m}^2)$ does happen. We observe first of all that (trivially) <u>any</u> set of generators of $\mathfrak{m}$ gives rise to a set of generators of $\mathfrak{m}/\mathfrak{m}^2$ over k. Hence $\dim_k(\mathfrak{m}/\mathfrak{m}^2)$ = smallest number of generators of $\mathfrak{m}$. Let now

$$R = \mathbb{C}[X, Y]/_{(Y^2 - X^3)} = \mathbb{C}[x, y]$$

$$\mathfrak{p} = xR + yR$$

$$A = R_{\mathfrak{p}}$$

$$\mathfrak{m} = \mathfrak{p}A_{\mathfrak{p}} \ .$$

We make (without proof) the following assertions: (b), c) have easy proofs)

a) dim R = 1

b) R is an integral domain

c) $\mathfrak{p}$ is prime

Hence it follows that $\mathfrak{p}$ is maximal and that $s(A) = \dim(A) = 1$. But $\mathfrak{m}$ is <u>not</u> principal, in fact $\dim_{A/\mathfrak{m}} (\mathfrak{m}/_{\mathfrak{m}^2}) = 2$. To see this, consider the diagram

$$\begin{array}{ccc} & \mathfrak{m} & — & A \\ & | & & | \\ \mathfrak{m} \cap R = & \mathfrak{p} & — & R \end{array}$$

We see that $\dim_{A/\mathfrak{m}} (\mathfrak{m}/_{\mathfrak{m}^2})$ = smallest no. of generators of $\mathfrak{m} \leqq 2$ (x, y generate $\mathfrak{m}$). However, were $\mathfrak{m}$ principal, so would $\mathfrak{p}$ be. Now were it so, the inverse image of $\mathfrak{p}$ under $\mathbb{C}[X, Y] \to R$ would be principal $\bmod(Y^2 - X^3)$, which is easily seen to be impossible. Hence $\dim_{\mathbb{C}}(\mathfrak{m}/_{\mathfrak{m}^2}) = 2$. (Note that $A/\mathfrak{m} = \mathbb{C}$). From dim R = 1 one obtains dim(A) = 1, whence $s(A) = 1 < \dim_{\mathbb{C}}(\mathfrak{m}/_{\mathfrak{m}^2})$.

When the local ring A is such that $s(A) = \dim_{A/\mathfrak{m}} (\mathfrak{m}/_{\mathfrak{m}^2})$ we say that A is a regular local ring.

The geometrical interpretation of the number $\dim_{A/\mathfrak{m}}(\mathfrak{m}/\mathfrak{m}^2)$ is the following: it is the number of linearly independent linear forms (modulo forms of higher degree). This corresponds to the classical concept of the dimension of the tangent space.

If A is not a local ring, one can still talk about dim(A), and one trivially gets the formula

$$\dim(A) = \operatorname{Sup}_{\mathfrak{m}}(\dim(A_{\mathfrak{m}}))$$

where $\mathfrak{m}$ ranges over the maximal ideals of A.

We give a brief description of the situation when dim(A) = 0, 1.

<u>dim(A) = 0</u>. Then A is artinian, hence semi-local. Let $\mathfrak{N}$ = nil radical(A). We get $A/\mathfrak{N} \simeq \oplus A/\mathfrak{m}_i$, i.e. $A/\mathfrak{N}$ is a direct sum of fields. Spec(A) consists of a finite number of closed points, and the local rings are <u>primary rings</u> (i.e. some power of the maximal ideal is 0). In fact, since A is artinian, so is $A_{\mathfrak{m}_i}$, whence $(\mathfrak{m}_i A_{\mathfrak{m}_i})^n = (\mathfrak{m}_i A_{\mathfrak{m}_i})^{n+1}$, $n \gg 0$, and $\bigcap_n (\mathfrak{m}_i A_{\mathfrak{m}_i})^n = (0)$. Furthermore we have

$$A = \Gamma(\operatorname{Spec} A, \tilde{A}) = \oplus A_{\mathfrak{m}_i}$$

which is easily seen from the fact that Spec(A) consists of a finite number of closed points.

<u>dim(A) = 1</u>. In this case the prime ideals of A are either minimal or maximal, and there are only finitely many minimal primes, with at least one, say $\mathfrak{p}$, such that $\dim(A/\mathfrak{p}) = 1$. If A is local, all minimal primes have this

property. There are infinitely many maximal primes, if A is not semi-local.

A typical example of this case are the Dedekind rings, i.e. noetherian, integrally closed domains A such that every prime ideal $\mathfrak{p} \subset A$, $\mathfrak{p} \neq (0)$ is maximal. It follows that all local rings $A_{\mathfrak{p}}$ are valuation rings.

We note however that, while in the case $A = \mathbb{C}[X]$ all local rings $A_{\mathfrak{p}}$ are isomorphic, when $A = Z$ we obtain distinct local rings, for distinct $\mathfrak{p}$.

One can get more one-dimensional examples in the following way: Let A be a Dedekind ring, K its field of quotients, L a finite extension of K. Then any ring B, with $A \subset B \subset L$, is one dimensional (and need not be Dedekind). (Krull-Akizuki theorem, B.C.A., VII, §2.) Other examples are the orders of A in L, i.e. rings contained in A, with field of quotients L (hence not integrally closed when they are different from A).

If A is one dimensional local ring which is a Dedekind domain (i.e. integrally closed), then A is a valuation ring (See Lang, "Introduction to Algebraic Geometry", theorem 1, p. 151, or B.C.A., VI).

The geometrical interpretation of the notion of Dedekind rings is seen by observing that, if A is a Dedekind domain, Spec(A) consists of one minimal prime and maximal primes whose local rings are integrally closed whence regular. Classically this corresponds to the notion of an irreducible, non-singular curve.

Let $A = \mathbb{C}[X, Y]$, and let $f(X, Y) \in \mathbb{C}[X, Y]$. Then a classical statement in Algebraic Geometry is that the irreducible components (in the Zariski topology) of the variety of zeros of $f(X, Y)$ have codimension $\leqq 1$. We generalize the above situation with the following:

Theorem 2.4. Let A be a noetherian ring, $x_1,\ldots,x_n \in A$, $\mathfrak{a} = x_1 A + \ldots + x_n A$. Let $\mathfrak{p}$ be a minimal prime in $\mathrm{Ass}(A/\mathfrak{a})$. Then $\mathrm{codim}(V(\mathfrak{p})) = \dim(A_{\mathfrak{p}}) \leqq n$

(When $n = 1$ this is the well-known "Hauptidealsatz").

Proof. We have the inclusions $A_{\mathfrak{p}} \supset \mathfrak{p} A_{\mathfrak{p}} \supset \mathfrak{a} A_{\mathfrak{p}}$. Since $\mathfrak{p}$ is minimal in $\mathrm{Ass}(A/\mathfrak{a})$, there are no primes of A properly included between $\mathfrak{p}$ and $\mathfrak{a}$, hence $A_{\mathfrak{p}}/\mathfrak{a} A_{\mathfrak{p}}$ has a unique prime ideal (namely $\mathfrak{p}(A_{\mathfrak{p}}/\mathfrak{a} A_{\mathfrak{p}})$), and is therefore Artinian, whence of finite length. Now $A_{\mathfrak{p}}/\mathfrak{a} A_{\mathfrak{p}} \simeq A_{\mathfrak{p}}/x_1 A_{\mathfrak{p}} + \ldots + x_n A_{\mathfrak{p}}$, whence $\mathrm{codim}(V(\mathfrak{p})) = \dim A_{\mathfrak{p}} = s(A_{\mathfrak{p}}) \leqq n$, Q.E.D.

Theorem 2.4 is an example of how we can apply our local dimension theory to a global situation.

Some final results concerning the notion of dimension:

Theorem 2.5. (Artin-Tate). Let A be a noetherian integral domain. Then the following conditions are equivalent:

a) A is semi-local of dimension $\leqq 1$

b) (0) is an isolated point in $\mathrm{Spec}(A)$

c) there exists an $f \in A$ such that A_f is a field.

Proof: We give a cyclic proof.

a) $\Longrightarrow$ b). Since A is integral, $(0) \in \mathrm{Spec}(A)$. Since A is semi-local, there are a finite number of closed points, $\{\mathfrak{m}_1\},\ldots,\{\mathfrak{m}_n\}$ in $\mathrm{Spec}(A)$. Since $\dim(A) \leqq 1$, $\mathrm{Spec}(A)$ consists precisely of $\{(0)\}$, $\{\mathfrak{m}_1\},\ldots,\{\mathfrak{m}_n\}$ and b) follows.

b) $\Longrightarrow$ c) Since (0) is isolated in Spec(A), and the open subsets $\{D(f)\}_{f \in A}$ form a basis for the Zariski topology of Spec(A), there exists $f \in A$ such that D(f) = (0). But D(f) = Spec A_f, whence A_f has <u>only one</u> prime ideal, namely (0), and c) follows.

c) $\Longrightarrow$ a) Let $\mathfrak{p} \neq (0)$ be any point of Spec(A). The injection $A \to A_f$ shows, since A_f is a field, that $1 \in \mathfrak{p} A_f$. Hence $f \in \mathfrak{p}$. We assert:

(*) every minimal prime ideal of A/fA is maximal.

In fact, since A/fA is noetherian, let $\mathfrak{p}_1, \ldots, \mathfrak{p}_k$ be the minimal prime ideals of A/fA. Assume that one of them, say $\mathfrak{p}_1$, is not maximal. Let $\mathfrak{m} \underset{\neq}{\supset} \mathfrak{p}_1$ be maximal. Since $\mathfrak{p}_j$ is minimal, we have $\mathfrak{m} \neq \mathfrak{p}_j$, $j = 2,\ldots,k$. If $\mathfrak{m} \subset \bigcup_{j=1}^{k} \mathfrak{p}_j$, then $\mathfrak{m} = \mathfrak{p}_j$ for some j, which we have just shown not to be the case. So $\mathfrak{m} \not\subset \bigcup_{j=1}^{k} \mathfrak{p}_j$ i.e. there exists $g' \in \mathfrak{m}$ such that $g' \notin \mathfrak{p}_j$, $j = 1,\ldots,k$. Let $g \in A$ such that $g' = g + fA$. Let $\mathfrak{q}$ be a minimal ideal of Ass(A/gA). By theorem 2.4 Codim(V($\mathfrak{q}$)) $\leqq 1$, and clearly Codim(V($\mathfrak{q}$)) = 1, since $\mathfrak{q} \neq (0)$ and A is an integral domain. Therefore $\mathfrak{q}$ is a minimal prime of A, hence $f \in \mathfrak{q}$ and $\mathfrak{q} \cdot A/fA$ is a minimal prime of A/fA, i.e. $\mathfrak{q} \cdot A/fA = \mathfrak{p}_j$ for some j. Clearly $g \in \mathfrak{q}$, hence $g' \in \mathfrak{p}_j$, is a contradiction. Therefore assertion (*) above is proved, and every non zero prime ideal of A is hence maximal. Furthermore the <u>only</u> prime ideals of A are (0) and the inverse images of $\mathfrak{p}_1, \ldots, \mathfrak{p}_k$. Hence A is semi-local and dim(A) = 1.

Proposition 2.6. Let A be a noetherian semi-local ring, M a finitely generated A-module, $x \in \mathfrak{N} = \mathrm{rad}(A)$. Then

$$\dim(M/xM) \geqq \dim(M) - 1$$

and equality holds if, and only if, x belongs to none of those minimal primes $\mathfrak{p} \in \mathrm{Ass}(M)$ such that $\dim(M) = \dim(A/\mathfrak{p})$.

Proof: By theorem 2.3 and lemma 2.1 we have

$$\dim(M/xM) = s(M/xM) \geqq s(M) - 1 = \dim(M) - 1.$$

Now assume that x belongs to none of those minimal primes $\mathfrak{p} \in \mathrm{Ass}(M)$ such that $\dim(M) = \dim(A/\mathfrak{p})$. Again by theorem 2.4 and lemma 2.1 we have

$$\dim(M/xM) \leqq \dim(M) - 1$$

whence equality holds. Conversely, assume that equality holds. Let $\mathfrak{p}_1, \ldots, \mathfrak{p}_k \in \mathrm{Ass}(M)$ such that $\dim(M) = \dim(A/\mathfrak{p}_j)$, $j = 1, \ldots, k$. Then clearly $\mathfrak{p}_j \notin \mathrm{Supp}(M/xM)$ (since, for any M, $\dim(M) = \dim(\mathrm{Supp}(M)) = \sup_{\mathfrak{p} \in \mathrm{Supp}(M)} (\dim A/\mathfrak{p}) = \sup_{\mathfrak{p} \in \mathrm{Ass}(M)} (\dim A/\mathfrak{p})$).

More quickly, since $\mathfrak{p}_j \in \mathrm{Supp}(M)$ and $\mathrm{Supp}(M/xM) = \mathrm{Supp}(M) \cap V(x)$, $x \notin \mathfrak{p}_j$. Q.E.D.

We define a notion extensively used in Algebraic Geometry.

Definition 2.5. Let A be a noetherian semi-local ring. A set of elements $x_1, \ldots, x_n \in \mathfrak{N}$ is called a system of parameters of the finitely generated A-module M if $n = \dim(M)$

and $M/x_1 M + \ldots + x_n M$ has finite length.

Note that, by the remark preceding definition 2.5 and theorem 2.4 every A-module admits a system of parameters.

We prove

Proposition 2.7. Let A, M be as in the above definition. Let $x_1, \ldots, x_k \in \mathfrak{n}$. Then

$$\dim(M/x_1 M + \ldots + x_k M) \geq n - k$$

and equality holds if, and only if, the system $x_1, \ldots, x_k$ can be imbedded in a system of parameters of M.

Proof: We proceed by induction on k.

When k = 1 the inequality holds by Proposition 2.6. Furthermore equality holds if and only if x belongs to none of the primes $\mathfrak{p}$ in Ass(M) with $\dim(M) = \dim(A/\mathfrak{p})$. Let $x_1, \ldots, x_{n-1} \in \mathfrak{n}$ such that $s(M/xM) = n - 1$, $(M/xM)/x_1(M/xM) + \ldots + x_{n-1}(M/xM)$ has finite length. (See definition 2.5) Then $x, x_1, \ldots, x_{n-1}$ is a system of parameters of M. Conversely, if x can be imbedded in a system of parameters, say $x, x_1, \ldots, x_{n-1}$ then $s(M/xM) \leq n - 1$ and, by Proposition 2.6, $\dim(M/xM) = n - 1$.

Q.E.D.

The equality

$$M/x_1 M + \ldots + x_k M = (M/x_1 M + \ldots + x_{k-1} M)/x_k(M/x_1 M + \ldots + x_{k-1} M)$$

shows, by the induction assumption, the desired inequality. Assume now $\dim(M/x_1 M + \ldots + x_k M) = n - k$. Then, letting $N = M/x_1 M$

$$\dim(N/x_2 N + \ldots + x_k N) = (n - 1) - (k - 1)$$

and

$$(n-1) - (k-1) \geqq \dim(N) - (k-1) \geqq \dim(M) - 1 - (k-1) = n-k$$

whence $\dim(N) - k + 1 = n - k$ or $\dim(N) = n - 1$. By the induction assumption, $\{x_2,\ldots,x_k\}$ can be imbedded in a system of parameters of N, say $\{x_2,\ldots,x_k, x_{k+1},\ldots,x_n\}$ (here we must use $\dim(N) = n - 1$). Then clearly $\{x_1, x_2,\ldots,x_n\}$ is a system of parameters of M.

Conversely, if $\{x_1, x_2,\ldots,x_k, x_{k+1},\ldots,x_n\}$ is a system of parameters of M, let $N = M/x_1 M$. Then $N/x_2 N +\ldots+x_n N$ has finite length, whence $s(N) \leqq n - 1$. By Proposition 2.6 we have

$$n - 1 = \dim(M) - 1 \leqq \dim(N) = s(N) \leqq n - 1$$

whence $\dim(N) = n - 1$. Hence $\{x_2,\ldots,x_k,\ldots,x_n\}$ is a system of parameters of N, and, by the induction assumption

$$\dim(N/x_2 N +\ldots+ x_k N) = (n - 1) - (k - 1) = n - k$$

The proposition is proved.

We finish this section with a few remarks about the nature of the function $\Psi:\mathrm{Spec}(A) \to \mathbb{N}$ given by

$$\Psi(\mathfrak{p}) = \dim(A_{\mathfrak{p}})$$

where A is any noetherian ring. It is obviously not continuous, otherwise it would have to be constant when Spec(A) is connected (e.g. when A is an integral domain), and trivial examples show this is not the case (say $A = k[X, Y]$).

We do nevertheless have some information, namely, by proposition 1.1,

$$\dim(A_{\mathfrak{p}}) \leqq \dim(A)$$

and

$$\dim(A/\mathfrak{p}) \leqq \dim(A).$$

The latter is geometrically interpreted as follows: If $x \in \overline{y}$, then $\dim(V(j_x)) \geqq \dim(V(j_y))$.

Dimension is a very coarse invariant, i.e. were we to consider the equivalence classes of affine varieties of a given dimension, we would obtain huge classes of highly non isomorphic varieties.

§3. DEPTH

The next numerical invariant we shall study in the notion of depth. We assume throughout this section that A is a noetherian local ring with maximal ideal $\mathfrak{m}$, and that M is a finitely generated A-module.

Definition 3.1. a) an element $x \in A$ is called M-regular if the homomorphism $\varphi: M \to M$ given by $\varphi(m) = xm$ is injective.

b) a sequence $\{x_1, \ldots, x_n\}$ of elements of A is called M-regular if x_i is $M/x_1 M + \ldots + x_{i-1} M$ regular, $1 \leqq i \leqq n$.

Remark. Clearly every $x \notin \mathfrak{m}$ being invertible is M-regular for every module M. Hence we shall confine our attention to those M-regular elements which belong to $\mathfrak{m}$. With regard to b) we state, without proof, the fact that the sequence $\{x_1, \ldots, x_n\}$ is M-regular if, and only if all sequences $\{x_{\sigma(1)}, \ldots, x_{\sigma(n)}\}$ $\sigma \in S_n$ are M-regular, where S_n denotes the group of permutations on n symbols. (Grothendieck, E.G.A., Ch. 0, §15.1, I.H.E.S. no 20) The above statement is false if A is not noetherian.

Clearly any sequence $\{x_1, \ldots, x_n\}$ with $x_1 \notin \mathfrak{m}$ is M-regular for every M (since $M/x_1 M = 0$), hence, keeping in mind the above remark, we shall confine our attention to M-regular sequences $\{x_1, \ldots, x_n\}$ with $x_i \in \mathfrak{m}$.

Definition 3.2. Depth (M) = maximal number of elements in all possible M-regular sequences (of elements of $\mathfrak{m}$!).

We investigate first some of the properties of the notion of M-regularity.

Proposition 3.1.

1) x is M-regular if, and only if, $x \notin \bigcup_{\mathfrak{p} \in \mathrm{Ass}(M)} \mathfrak{p}$.

2) if x is M-regular, $\dim(M/xM) = \dim(M) - 1$.

3) any M-regular sequence is contained in a system of parameters of M.

4) the sequence $\{x_1, \ldots, x_r\}$ is a maximal M-regular sequence if, and only if, one of the following two equivalent conditions hold

   i) $\mathrm{Hom}_A(k, M/x_1 M + \ldots + x_r M) \neq 0$, where $k = A/\mathfrak{m}$.

   ii) $M/x_1 M + \ldots + x_r M$ contains a submodule isomorphic to k.

5) let $\{x_1, \ldots, x_r\}$ be an M-regular sequence. Then $\mathrm{Hom}_A(k, M/x_1 M + \ldots + x_r M) \cong \mathrm{Ext}_A{}^r(k, M) \cong \mathrm{Ext}_A{}^{r-1}(k, M/x_1 M)$.

Proof: 1) Assume x is M-regular, and $x \in \bigcup_{\mathfrak{p} \in \mathrm{Ass}(M)} \mathfrak{p}$. Then $x \in \mathfrak{p} \in \mathrm{Ass}(M)$, for some $\mathfrak{p}$. Now $\mathfrak{p}$ is the annihilator of some $m \neq 0$, $m \in M$. Therefore the homomorphism

$\varphi : M \to M$, $\varphi(m') = xm'$ is not injective ($\varphi(m) = 0$, $m \neq 0$).

Conversely, assume $x \notin \bigcup_{\mathfrak{p} \in \mathrm{Ass}(M)} \mathfrak{p}$, and let $m \neq 0$, $m \in M$ such that $xm = 0$. Since $m \neq 0$, $0 \neq Am \subset M$, hence $\mathrm{Ass}(Am) \neq \emptyset$ (in fact $M = 0 \iff \mathrm{Ass}(M) = \emptyset$). Now $\mathrm{Ass}(Am) \subset \mathrm{Ass}(M)$ trivially, and $x \in \mathrm{Ann}(Am)$, whence $x \in \bigcap_{\mathfrak{p} \in \mathrm{Ass}(Am)} \mathfrak{p}$, a contradiction.

2) This is an immediate consequence of 1) and proposition 2.6.

3) We prove this by induction on k, where $\{x_1, \ldots, x_k\}$ is an M-regular sequence. If $k = 1$, then x_1 is M-regular and, by 2) above and Proposition 2.7, $\{x_1\}$ can be imbedded in a system of parameters of M. Let $k > 1$. By induction assumption and Proposition 2.7,

$$\dim(M/x_1 M + \ldots + x_{k-1} M) = \dim(M) - k + 1,$$

and from $M/x_1 M + \ldots + x_k M = (M/x_1 M + \ldots + x_{k-1} M)/ x_k(M/x_1 M + \ldots + x_{k-1} M)$ and 2) above we get (since x_k is $M/x_1 M + \ldots + x_{k-1}$ M-regular):

$$\dim(M/x_1 M + \ldots + x_k M) = \dim(M) - k$$

whence, again from Proposition 2.7, $\{x_1, \ldots, x_k\}$ can be imbedded in a system of parameters of M.

4) We observe that a sequence $\{x_1, \ldots, x_r\}$ is M-regular and maximal if, and only if, the sequence $\{x_2, \ldots, x_r\}$ is M/x_1 M-regular and maximal, hence we are reduced by induction to the case $r = 0$. We observe furthermore that conditions i) and ii) are obviously equivalent, since a non zero A-homomorphism

of $k = A/\mathfrak{m}$ is injective.

Now $r = 0$ (and maximality), implies that there are no M-regular elements in $\mathfrak{m}$, and by 1) above $\mathfrak{m} = \bigcup_{\mathfrak{p} \in \mathrm{Ass}(M)} \mathfrak{p}$. Therefore $\mathfrak{m} \in \mathrm{Ass}(M)$ and, $\mathfrak{m}$ being the annihilator of some non zero $x \in M$, $k = A/\mathfrak{m} \simeq Ax \subset M$ and ii) follows. Conversely, if $M \supset N \simeq A/\mathfrak{m} = k$, let $x \in M$ be a generator of N. Then $\mathfrak{m}$ is the annihilator of x, whence $\mathfrak{m} \in \mathrm{Ass}(M)$ and there are no M-regular elements in $\mathfrak{m}$, i.e. $\emptyset$ is a maximal sequence of M-regular elements, Q.E.D.

5) Let $N = M/x_1 M$. We have an exact sequence

$$0 \to M \xrightarrow{\varphi} M \xrightarrow{c} N \to 0$$

where $\varphi(m) = x_1 m$. Hence we get

$$\ldots \to \mathrm{Ext}_A^{r-1}(k, M) \xrightarrow{\tilde{\varphi}} \mathrm{Ext}_A^{r-1}(k, M) \xrightarrow{\tilde{c}}$$

$$\mathrm{Ext}_A^{r-1}(k, N) \xrightarrow{\partial} \mathrm{Ext}_A^{r}(k, M) \xrightarrow{\tilde{\varphi}} \mathrm{Ext}_A^{r}(k, M) \to \ldots$$

Now, since $x_1 \in \mathfrak{m}$, $\tilde{\varphi} = 0$ (multiplication by x_1 annihilates all elements of k). On the other hand, by induction

$$\mathrm{Ext}_A^{r-1}(k, M) \cong \mathrm{Hom}(k, M/x_1 M + \ldots + x_{r-1} M) = 0$$

since $\{x_1, \ldots, x_{r-1}\}$ is not a maximal M-regular sequence. Therefore $\mathrm{Ext}_A^{r-1}(k, N) \cong \mathrm{Ext}_A^{r}(k, M)$. As was pointed out in the proof of 4), $\{x_2, \ldots, x_r\}$ is a maximal N-regular sequence, whence we can proceed by induction and obtain

$$\mathrm{Ext}_A^{r-1}(k, N) \cong \mathrm{Ext}_A^{r-2}(k, M/x_1 M + x_2 M) \cong \ldots$$

$$\cong \mathrm{Hom}(k, M/x_1 M + \ldots + x_r M),$$

and 5) is proved.

Corollary 3.1. Maximal M-regular sequences have the same cardinality.

Proof: Obvious from 5).

Corollary 3.2. Let $M^n = \bigoplus_{i=1}^{n} M_i,\ M_i \simeq M$. Then Depth (M^k) = Depth (M).

Proof: The isomorphism

$$M^n/x_1M^n+\ldots+x_rM^n = M/x_1M+\ldots+x_rM \oplus\ldots\oplus M/x_1M+\ldots+x_rM$$

shows that any maximal M^n regular sequence is a maximal M-regular sequence. The corollary follows from Corollary 3.1.

We now come to the main theorem concerning the notion of depth, namely:

Theorem 3.1. Let A be a noetherian local ring, M a finitely generated A-module. Then

i) depth (M) = 0 is equivalent to $\mathfrak{m} \in \mathrm{Ass}(M)$.

ii) if $x \in \mathfrak{m}$ is M-regular then depth (M/xM) = depth (M) - 1.

iii) depth (M) $\leqq \inf_{\mathfrak{p} \in \mathrm{Ass}(M)} \dim(A/\mathfrak{p}) \leqq \sup_{\mathfrak{p} \in \mathrm{Ass}(M)} \dim(A/\mathfrak{p})$ = dim(M).

Proof: i) This is a restatement of 1), Proposition 3.1.

ii) Let $\{x_2,\ldots,x_r\}$ be a maximal M/xM-regular sequence. If x is M-regular, then $\{x, x_2,\ldots,x_r\}$ is a maximal M-regular sequence, whence depth (M) = depth (M/xM) + 1.

iii) We prove this by induction on n = depth (M). If n = 0, then $\mathfrak{m} \in \mathrm{Ass}(M)$, whence, trivially

$$0 = \inf_{\mathfrak{p} \in \mathrm{Ass}(M)} \dim(A/\mathfrak{p}) \leqq \sup_{\mathfrak{p} \in \mathrm{Ass}(M)} \dim(A/\mathfrak{p}) = \dim(M).$$

In the induction step we shall make use of the following:

Lemma 3.1. Let $t \in \mathfrak{m}$ be M-regular, $\mathfrak{p} \in \mathrm{Ass}(M)$. Then any minimal prime containing $\mathfrak{p} + At$ belongs to $\mathrm{Ass}(M/tM)$.

Proof: By Proposition 4 of B.C.A., IV, §1, there exists a submodule $M' \subset M$ and an exact sequence

$$0 \to M' \to M \to M'' \to 0$$

such that $\mathrm{Ass}(M') = \{\mathfrak{p}\}$; $\mathrm{Ass}(M'') = \mathrm{Ass}(M) - \{\mathfrak{p}\}$. By 1 of Proposition 3.1, t is both M'-regular and M"-regular and the diagram

$$\begin{array}{ccccccccc}
 & & 0 & & 0 & & 0 & & \\
 & & \downarrow & & \downarrow & & \downarrow & & \\
0 & \to & M' & \to & M & \to & M'' & \to & 0 \\
 & & \downarrow & & \downarrow & & \downarrow & & \\
0 & \to & M' & \to & M & \to & M'' & \to & 0 \\
 & & \downarrow & & \downarrow & & \downarrow & & \\
0 & \to & M'/tM' & \to & M/tM & \to & M''/tM'' & \to & 0 \\
 & & \downarrow & & \downarrow & & \downarrow & & \\
 & & 0 & & 0 & & 0 & &
\end{array}$$

is obviously commutative and exact, whence $\mathrm{Ass}(M'/tM') \subset \mathrm{Ass}(M/tM)$. We have

$$\mathrm{Supp}(M'/tM') = \mathrm{Supp}(M') \cap V(t).$$

If $\mathfrak{q}$ is a minimal prime containing $\mathfrak{p} + At$, then from the above $\mathfrak{q}$ is a minimal prime of $\mathrm{Supp}(M'/tM')$, whence $\mathfrak{q} \in \mathrm{Ass}(M'/tM)$ and we are done.

We return to the proof of iii) of theorem 3.1. Assume depth $(M) = n$. Let $x \in \mathfrak{m}$ be M-regular, $N = M/xM$. By ii) of theorem 3.1, depth $(N) = n - 1$. Let $\mathfrak{p}$ be any point in

Ass(M), and let $\mathfrak{q}$ be a minimal prime containing $\mathfrak{p}$ + Ax. Clearly $\mathfrak{q} \supsetneq \mathfrak{p}$ (since $x \notin \mathfrak{p}$) and by the lemma $\mathfrak{q} \in$ Ass(N). By the induction assumption we have

$$n - 1 \leqq \dim(A/\mathfrak{q})$$

and clearly $\dim(A/\mathfrak{q}) \leqq \dim(A/\mathfrak{p}) - 1$. Hence $n \leqq \dim(A/\mathfrak{p})$, for all $\mathfrak{p} \in$ Ass(M), iii) follows.

$\longleftrightarrow$

Appendix

Not only is the function d:Spec(A) $\to$ N given by $d(\mathfrak{p})$ = depth $(A_{\mathfrak{p}})$ not continuous, but the concept of depth is a considerably more sensitive invariant than dimension. In particular depth $(A_{\mathfrak{p}})$ bears no relation to depth (A), contrary to the behavior of dimension. To see this, let A be any local ring, which is an integral domain, $\mathfrak{p} \in$ Spec(A), say $\mathfrak{p}$ = (0). Then $A_{\mathfrak{p}}$ is a field, and has hence depth 0, while depth (A) is arbitrary. On the other hand let A_o be any local integral domain, $\mathfrak{m}_o$ its unique maximal ideal, $k_o = A_o/\mathfrak{m}_o$. Consider the A_o-module $A = A_o \oplus k_o$, and define on A a ring structure by defining $(a, x)\cdot(a', x') = (aa', ax' + a'x)$. One easily checks that A is a local ring, with $\mathfrak{m}_o \oplus k_o$ as unique maximal ideal, and that every non-unit in A is a zero divisor, whence depth (A) = 0. However, if $\dim(A_o) \geqq 2$, and $\mathfrak{p}_o$ is a non zero, non maximal prime ideal of A_o then $\mathfrak{p} = \mathfrak{p}_o \oplus k_o$ is a prime ideal in A and $A_{\mathfrak{p}} \simeq A_{o\,\mathfrak{p}_o}$. Now depth $(A_{o\,\mathfrak{p}_o}) \geqq 1$ since $A_{o\,\mathfrak{p}_o}$ is an integral domain.

The following result is due to Hartshorne and gives a geometrical significance to the notion of depth.

(Hartshorne) Let A be a local ring with depth (A) $\geqq 2$. Then Spec(A) - $\{\mathfrak{m}\}$ is a connected topological space.

In particular, the local ring of the unique point of intersection of two sufficiently general planes in four dimensional affine space is a 2-dimensional ring whose depth (by Hartshorne's result) is $\leqq 1$. This shows that, in the inequalities iii) of Theorem 3.1, strict inequality is possible. This justifies the following:

Definition 3.3. Let A be a noetherian local ring, M a finitely generated A-module. M is said to be a Cohen-Macaulay module (C-M module) if depth (M) = dim(M). If A is an arbitrary noetherian ring (not necessarily local), A is said to be a Cohen-Macaulayring if, for every maximal ideal $\mathfrak{m}$ of A, the local ring $A_{\mathfrak{m}}$ is Cohen-Macaulay.

We illustrate the notion of C-M modules with a few examples.

1) dim(M) = 0, M $\neq$ 0. Then, from iii) of theorem 3.1, M is C-M. Here the notion of C-M modules is redundant.
2) dim(A) = 1, A a noetherian local ring. Then, if A is C-M, depth (A) = 1, which is equivalent to saying, since dim(A) = 1, that $\mathfrak{m} \notin$ Ass(A). Hence a non C-M ring of dimension 1 is a local ring in which all non-units are zero divisors. For example if A = k[x, y], where k is any field and $x^2 y = xy^2 = 0$, and $\mathfrak{m} = xA + yA$, one easily checks that $A_{\mathfrak{m}}$ is a non C-M ring of dimension 1.

3) $\dim(A) = 2$. Here we limit ourselves to showing that every 2-dimensional, integrally closed local integral domain is C-M. To see this, let $x \in \mathfrak{m}$, $x \neq 0$. Since A is an integral domain, x is A-regular and, since A is integrally closed, none of the prime ideals associated to xA is imbedded (see B.C.A., VII, §1). Then, if $\mathfrak{p} \in \mathrm{Ass}(A/xA)$, it follows by the Hauptidealsatz that $\mathfrak{p} \neq \mathfrak{m}$.

Therefore $\mathfrak{m} = \bigcup_{\mathfrak{p} \in \mathrm{Ass}(A/xA)} \mathfrak{p}$ is impossible, and a $y \in \mathfrak{m}$, $y \notin \bigcup_{\mathfrak{p} \in \mathrm{Ass}(A/xA)} \mathfrak{p}$ can be found. Therefore depth $(A) \geqq 2$, and hence depth $(A) = 2 = \dim(A)$ which proves our assertion.

We now investigate some of the consequences of knowing that a ring A, or a module M, are C-M.

<u>Proposition 3.2</u>. Let M be a C-M A-module. Then

1) For every $\mathfrak{p} \in \mathrm{Ass}(M)$,

$$\dim(A/\mathfrak{p}) = \dim(M) = \mathrm{depth}\ (M)$$

2) The following three conditions are equivalent:

(i) x is M-regular

(ii) $\dim(M/xM) = \dim(M) - 1$

(iii) x belongs to no prime of Ass(M)

3) If x is M-regular, M/xM is a C-M module

<u>Proof</u>: 1) is a trivial consequence of the definition of C-M modules and of (iii) of Theorem 3.1.

2) (i) implies (ii) by (ii) of Theorem 3.1, and (i) is equivalent to (iii) by 1) of Proposition 3.1. It remains to prove that (ii) implies (i). This follows immediately from 1)

above (all primes in Ass(M) are equidimensional) and proposition 2.6.

3) By (ii) of Theorem 3.1 we have

$$\text{depth }(M/xM) = \text{depth }(M) - 1 = \dim(M) - 1 = \dim(M/xM)$$

hence M/xM is a C-M module.

We state without proof (an easy application of proposition 2.7 and 3.1) the generalization of 2) and 3) above to M-regular sequences.

Proposition 3.3. Let M be a C-M module. Then the following three conditions are equivalent:

(i) $\{x_1,\ldots,x_r\}$ is an M-regular sequence

(ii) $\dim(M/x_1 M +\ldots+ x_r M) = \dim(M) - r$

(iii) $\{x_1,\ldots,x_r\}$ is embeddable in a system of parameters.

Furthermore, if $\{x_1,\ldots,x_r\}$ is an M-regular sequence, then $M/x_1 M +\ldots+ x_r M$ is a C-M module.

Proposition 3.4. A module M, for which conditions (i), (ii), (iii) of the previous proposition are equivalent, and such that $M/x_1 M +\ldots+ x_r M$ is C-M whenever $\{x_1,\ldots,x_r\}$ is an M regular sequence, is a C-M module.

Proof: Let $n = \dim(M)$. If $n = 0$ there is nothing to prove. Assume $n \geqq 1$, let $\{x_1,\ldots,x_n\}$ be a system of parameters of M. Since (iii) $\Longrightarrow$ (i), x_1 is M-regular and $M/x_1 M$ is a C-M module. Now since x_1 is M-regular $x_1 \notin \bigcup_{\mathfrak{p} \in \mathrm{Ass}(M)} \mathfrak{p}$, whence $\dim(M/x_1 M) = \dim(M) - 1$. Therefore

$$\dim(M) = \dim(M/x_1M) + 1 = \operatorname{depth}(M/x_1M) + 1 = \operatorname{depth}(M)$$

and M is C-M, Q.E.D.

Corollary 3.3. If M is a C-M module, every maximal M-regular sequence is a system of parameters and conversely.

Proof: Obvious.

Remark. If A is a (not necessarily local) C-M integral domain, and $x \in A$, $x \neq 0$, clearly x is A-regular, whence A/xA is again C-M. Since $k[X_1, \ldots, X_n]$ is a C-M ring (we shall prove this later), it follows from the above remark that, if $f(X_1, \ldots, X_n)$, $g(X_1, \ldots, X_n)$ are relatively prime irreducible elements of $k[X_1, \ldots, X_n]$, then $k[X_1, \ldots, X_n]/(f, g)$ is again C-M. This throws a better light on example 2) given after definition 3.3.

We now examine the behavior of the notion of C-M under localization. We have

Proposition 3.5. Let M be a C-M module, $\mathfrak{p} \in \operatorname{Supp}(M)$. Then

1) $M_{\mathfrak{p}} = M \otimes A_{\mathfrak{p}}$ is a C-M module
2) $\dim(M) = \dim(M_{\mathfrak{p}}) + \dim(M/\mathfrak{p}M)$

Proof: We shall obtain proposition 3.5 as a consequence of the following:

Proposition 3.6. Let M be a C-M module, $\mathfrak{p} \in \operatorname{Supp}(M)$, $r = \dim(M) - \dim(M/\mathfrak{p}M)$. Then

1) There exists an M-regular sequence $\{x_1, \ldots, x_r\}$ with $x_i \in \mathfrak{p}$ and

2) any such sequence gives

$$\dim(M/x_1 M + \ldots + x_r M) = \dim(M/\mathfrak{p} M) = \dim(A/\mathfrak{p}).$$

Proof: To prove 1) we proceed by induction on r. When $r = 0$ the statement is trivial. Let $r \geqq 1$. Then $\dim(M/\mathfrak{p} M) < \dim(M)$, hence $\mathfrak{p} \notin \mathrm{Ass}(M)$ (since the primes in Ass(M) are equidimensional), and therefore $\mathfrak{p} \not\subset \bigcup_{\mathfrak{q} \in \mathrm{Ass}(M)} \mathfrak{q}$.
Let $x_1 \in \mathfrak{p}$, $x_1 \notin \bigcup_{\mathfrak{q} \in \mathrm{Ass}(M)} \mathfrak{q}$. Then x_1 is M-regular and the module $N = M/x_1 M$ is C-M. Furthermore $\dim(N) = \dim(M) - 1$ and $N/\mathfrak{p} N \simeq M/\mathfrak{p} M$. We can hence apply the induction assumption to N and find an N-regular sequence $\{x_1, \ldots, x_r\}$ with $x_i \in \mathfrak{p}$. Now trivially $\{x_1, \ldots, x_r\}$ is an M-regular sequence with $x_i \in \mathfrak{p}$, and 1) is proved. 2) Let $\{x_1, \ldots, x_r\}$ be an M-regular sequence with $x_i \in \mathfrak{p}$. Let $P = M/x_1 M + \ldots + x_r M$ ($P = M$ if $r = 0$). Now $P/\mathfrak{p} P = M/\mathfrak{p} M$ and from proposition 3.3 we get that

$$\dim(P/\mathfrak{p} P) = \dim(M) - r = \dim(P)$$

and that P is a C-M module. Now clearly $\mathfrak{p} \in \mathrm{Supp}(P)$, hence $\mathfrak{p} \supset \mathfrak{p}_0'$ for some $\mathfrak{p}_0' \in \mathrm{Ass}(P)$. Furthermore we have $\dim(P/\mathfrak{p} P) = \dim(P) = \dim(A/\mathfrak{p}')$ for <u>all</u> $\mathfrak{p}' \in \mathrm{Ass}(P)$ (since P is C-M). Since clearly $\mathfrak{p} \subset \mathrm{Ann}(P/\mathfrak{p} P)$

$$\dim(P) = \dim(P/\mathfrak{p} P) \leqq \dim(A/\mathfrak{p})$$

and $\dim(A/\mathfrak{p}) \leqq \dim(A/\mathfrak{p}_0') = \dim(P)$. Hence $\mathfrak{p} = \mathfrak{p}_0'$ i.e. $\mathfrak{p} \in \mathrm{Ass}(P)$ and 2) follows.

We now prove Proposition 3.5. Let $x_1, \ldots, x_r$ be an M-regular sequence in $\mathfrak{p}$, where $r = \dim(M) - \dim(M/\mathfrak{p}M)$. Since localization is a flat operation we have that the images of $x_1, \ldots, x_r$ in $\mathfrak{p}M_{\mathfrak{p}}$ are still an $M_{\mathfrak{p}}$-regular sequence. Hence by proposition 1.1

$$\dim(M_{\mathfrak{p}}) \leqq \dim(M) - \dim(M/\mathfrak{p}M) = r \leqq \operatorname{depth}(M_{\mathfrak{p}}) \leqq \dim(M_{\mathfrak{p}})$$

whence 1) and 2) of proposition 3.5 follow.

Corollary 3.4. If A is a local C-M ring, A is catenary, and for every local epimorphism $A \to B$, B is catenary.

Proof: The quotient of a catenary local ring by a prime ideal being catenary, it is enough to prove A is catenary. Let $\mathfrak{w}$ be a minimal prime ideal of A, $\mathfrak{p}$, $\mathfrak{q}$ two prime ideals of A such that $\mathfrak{w} \subset \mathfrak{p} \subset \mathfrak{q}$. Then $A_{\mathfrak{q}}$ is a C-M ring and

$$\dim(A_{\mathfrak{q}}) = \dim(A_{\mathfrak{p}}) + \dim(A_{\mathfrak{q}}/\mathfrak{p}A_{\mathfrak{q}})$$

by proposition 3.5. If $A' = A/\mathfrak{w}$, and $\mathfrak{p}'$, $\mathfrak{q}'$ are the images of $\mathfrak{p}$, $\mathfrak{q}$ in A', this relation is equivalent to

$$\dim(A'_{\mathfrak{q}'}) = \dim(A'_{\mathfrak{p}'}) + \dim(A'_{\mathfrak{q}'}/\mathfrak{p}'A'_{\mathfrak{q}'})$$

hence A' is catenary by proposition 1.2; this shows that A itself is catenary.

Remark. The notion of C-M rings still is insufficient to distinguish the three local rings considered in the introduction, i.e. $\mathbb{C}[X, Y]/(Y^2 - X^3 - X^2)$; $\mathbb{C}[X, Y]/(Y^2 - X^3)$; $\mathbb{C}[X, Y](X - Y)$, localized at the origin. One easily checks that all three are C-M rings, following the procedure used in the remark after Corollary 3.3.

We shall obtain one notion which distinguishes the three local rings in the next section.

§4. REGULAR RINGS

We let A be a noetherian local ring, $\mathfrak{m}$ its maximal ideal, $k = A/\mathfrak{m}$. We denote by $S_k(\mathfrak{m}/\mathfrak{m}^2)$ the symmetric algebra of the k-vector space $\mathfrak{m}/\mathfrak{m}^2$. If $\text{rank}_k(\mathfrak{m}/\mathfrak{m}^2) = r$ one trivially has $S_k(\mathfrak{m}/\mathfrak{m}^2) \simeq k[T_1,\ldots,T_r]$ = where $T_1,\ldots,T_r$ are indeterminates over k.

We proceed to define a homomorphism

$$\theta : S_k(\mathfrak{m}/\mathfrak{m}^2) \to gr_{\mathfrak{m}}(A) = \bigoplus_{i=0}^{\infty} \mathfrak{m}^i/\mathfrak{m}^{i+1}$$

as follows:

Let $\overline{x}_1,\ldots,\overline{x}_r$ be a k-basis of $\mathfrak{m}/\mathfrak{m}^2$, and let $x_1,\ldots,x_r \in \mathfrak{m}$ be their representatives. By Nakayama's Lemma (see the remark on page 35) $x_1,\ldots,x_r$ forms a set of generators of $\mathfrak{m}$. Hence $\mathfrak{m}^i$ is generated by elements of the form $x_1^{\alpha_1} \ldots x_r^{\alpha_r}$ with $\alpha_1 + \ldots + \alpha_r = i$. θ is defined by $\theta(\overline{x}_1^{\alpha_1} \ldots \overline{x}_r^{\alpha_r})$ = the class of $x_1^{\alpha_1} \ldots x_r^{\alpha_r} \bmod \mathfrak{m}^{i+1}$. Trivially θ is a homogeneous homomorphism of degree 0, and an epimorphism.

<u>Theorem 4.1</u>. Let A be a noetherian local ring of dimension n, $\mathfrak{m}$ its maximal ideal $k = A/\mathfrak{m}$. The following four conditions are equivalent.

a) $\theta : S_k(\mathfrak{m}/\mathfrak{m}^2) \to gr_{\mathfrak{m}}(A)$ is bijective

b) $\text{rank}_k(\mathfrak{m}/\mathfrak{m}^2) = n$

c) $\mathfrak{m}$ is generated by n elements

d) There exists an A-regular system which generates $\mathfrak{m}$.

<u>Proof</u>: b) $\Longrightarrow$ c) follows from the remark above that every k-basis of $\mathfrak{m}/\mathfrak{m}^2$ lifts back (in $\mathfrak{m}$) to a set of generators of $\mathfrak{m}$ (by Nakayama's Lemma). Conversely, any set of generators of $\mathfrak{m}$ gives rise (mod $\mathfrak{m}^2$) to a set of generators of $\mathfrak{m}/\mathfrak{m}^2$ over k, whence $\operatorname{rank}_k(\mathfrak{m}/\mathfrak{m}^2) \leqq n$. But, by proposition 2.5, $\operatorname{rank}_k(\mathfrak{m}/\mathfrak{m}^2) \geqq n$, whence c) $\Longrightarrow$ b). We have proved <u>b) $\Longleftrightarrow$ c)</u>.

a) $\Longrightarrow$ d). Let $\overline{z}_1,\ldots,\overline{z}_r \in \mathfrak{m}/\mathfrak{m}^2$ be a basis of $\mathfrak{m}/\mathfrak{m}^2$ over k. We use the symbol $\overline{z}^\alpha$ for $\overline{z}_1^{\alpha_1} \ldots \overline{z}_r^{\alpha_r}$, and $|\alpha| = \alpha_1 +\ldots+ \alpha_r$. Let $z_1,\ldots,z_r \in \mathfrak{m}$ be representatives of $\overline{z}_1,\ldots,\overline{z}_r$. We already know that $z_1,\ldots,z_r$ generate $\mathfrak{m}$ (Nakayama's Lemma), and shall show that they form an A-regular sequence. We begin by asserting that, obviously,

$$\theta\Big(\sum_{|\alpha|=j} \overline{c}_\alpha \overline{z}^\alpha\Big) = \sum_{|\alpha|=j} c_\alpha z^\alpha \pmod{\mathfrak{m}^{j+1}}$$

where $\overline{c}_\alpha \in k = A/\mathfrak{m}$, $c_\alpha \in A$, their representatives. Hence, since θ is injective, the relation $\sum_{|\alpha|=j} c_\alpha z^\alpha \in \mathfrak{m}^{j+1}$, $c_\alpha \in A$ implies $\theta\Big(\sum_{|\alpha|=j} \overline{c}_\alpha \overline{z}^\alpha\Big) = 0$, whence $c_\alpha \in \mathfrak{m}$.

Assume now that $z_1,\ldots,z_r$ do not form an A-regular sequence. Then, for some j, $1 \leqq j \leqq r$, there exists an $x \in A$, $x \notin A z_1 +\ldots+ A z_{j-1}$ and $xz_j \in A z_1 +\ldots+ A z_{j-1}$. That, is we have an equation of the form

$$xz_j = y_1 z_1 +\ldots+ y_{j-1} z_{j-1}.$$

Since θ is surjective, we have, for some t,

$$xz_j = \sum_{|\alpha|=t} c_\alpha z_j z^\alpha \qquad (\text{mod. } \mathfrak{m}^{t+2})$$

where at least one c_α for an α with $\alpha_1 = \alpha_2 = \ldots = \alpha_{j-1} = 0$ is such that $c_\alpha \notin \mathfrak{m}$. However, in the expression of $y_1 z_1 + \ldots + y_{j-1} z_{j-1}$ as $\sum_{|\alpha| \leqq t+1} d_\alpha z^\alpha$ (mod. $\mathfrak{m}^{t+2}$), all the coefficients d_α such that $d_\alpha \notin \mathfrak{m}$ correspond to multiindices α for which $\alpha_1, \alpha_2, \ldots, \alpha_{j-1}$ are not all 0. We thus reach a contradiction.

d) $\Longrightarrow$ c). Let $z_1, \ldots, z_r$ be an A-regular sequence which forms a set of generators of $\mathfrak{m}$. Then, by proposition 2.5,

$$r \geqq \text{rank}_k(\mathfrak{m}/\mathfrak{m}^2) \geqq n$$

and by the definition of depth (A) and theorem 3.1

$$n \geqq \text{depth (A)} \geqq r.$$

Hence $r = \text{rank}_k(\mathfrak{m}/\mathfrak{m}^2) = n$, and c) follows:

c) $\Longrightarrow$ a). We proceed by contradition, i.e. we assume $\ker \theta \neq 0$. For brevity's sake we write $S = S_k(\mathfrak{m}/\mathfrak{m}^2)$; $G = \text{gr}_{\mathfrak{m}}(A)$. We have the exact sequence

$$0 \rightarrow \mathfrak{J} \rightarrow S \xrightarrow{\theta} G \rightarrow 0$$

with $\mathfrak{J} \neq 0$. Since θ is homogeneous, $\mathfrak{J}$ is a homogeneous ideal in S, and $\mathfrak{J}_0 = \mathfrak{J}_1 = 0$, since $S_0 = G_0 = k$, $S_1 = G_1 = \mathfrak{m}/\mathfrak{m}^2$. Let h be the smallest positive integer such that $\mathfrak{J}_h \neq 0$. Let $u \in \mathfrak{J}_h$, $u \neq 0$. Then clearly, S being an integral domain, $S_{s-h} \tilde{\to} uS_{s-h}$, $s \geqq h$ ($a \to ua$) and $uS_{s-h} \subset \mathfrak{J}_s$. Hence, (since $\text{rank}_k(\mathfrak{m}/\mathfrak{m}^2) = n$, by c) $\Longrightarrow$ b)),

$$\text{length}_k(\mathfrak{J}_s) \geqq \text{length}_k(S_{s-h}) = \binom{s-h+n-1}{n-1}$$

The exact sequence

$$0 \to \mathfrak{J}_s \to S_s \to G_s \to 0$$

shows $\text{length}_k(G_s) = \text{length}_k(S_s) - \text{length}_k(\mathfrak{J}_s) =$

$$= \binom{s+n-1}{n-1} - \text{length}_k(\mathfrak{J}_s) \leqq \binom{s+n-1}{n-1} - \binom{s-h+n-1}{n-1}$$

and $\binom{s+n-1}{n-1} - \binom{s-h+n-1}{n-1}$ is a polynomial in s of degree at most $(n-2)$.

From the exact sequence

$$0 \to G_s \to A/\mathfrak{m}^{s+1} \to A/\mathfrak{m}^s \to 0$$

we have, with the notations of section 2,

$$\text{length}(G_s) = P_{\mathfrak{m}}(A, s+1) - P_{\mathfrak{m}}(A, s).$$

By theorem 2.3 and a well-known result of polynomial theory we have

$$P_{\mathfrak{m}}(A, s) = c_n\binom{s+n}{n} + c_{n+1}\binom{s+n-1}{n-1} + \dots c_0,$$

with $c_i \in \mathbb{Q}$ (actually, since $P_{\mathfrak{m}}(A, s) \in \mathbb{Z}$, one easily sees that

$c_i \in Z$), and $c_n \neq 0$. Hence $P_{\mathfrak{m}}(A, s+1) - P_{\mathfrak{m}}(A, s) = c_n\binom{s+n}{n-1}$ + terms of lower degree. Hence length(G_s) is a polynomial of degree $n - 1$ for $s >> 0$. We have reached a contradiction and a) is proved. If dim(A) = 0, $\mathfrak{m}$ = (0) and the theorem is trivial. The theorem is proved.

Definition 4.1. A local ring A is said to be regular if it satisfies either a), b), c), or d) of theorem 4.1.

Corollary 4.1. Let A be a regular local ring. Then

i) A is an integral domain

ii) A is C-M

iii) A is integrally closed.

Proof: i) $S_k(\mathfrak{m}/\mathfrak{m}^2)$ is trivially an integral domain; by a) of theorem 4.1 so is $gr_{\mathfrak{m}}(A)$. Hence A cannot have zero divisors. (B.C.A., III, 2,3).

ii) In the proof of d) ⟹ c) in theorem 4.1 we showed

$$r \leq \text{depth}(A) \leq \dim(A) \leq \text{rank}_k(\mathfrak{m}/\mathfrak{m}^2) \leq r$$

where r is the number of elements in an A-regular sequence which generates $\mathfrak{m}$. Hence depth(A) = dim(A) and A is C-M.

iii) $S_k(\mathfrak{m}/\mathfrak{m}^2)$ is trivially integrally closed B.C.A., V., §1 Corollary 3. Hence so is $gr_{\mathfrak{m}}(A)$, and by proposition 15 of B.C.A., V, §1, A is integrally closed.

We give some examples of regular local rings. It is clear from c) of theorem 4.1 that if dim(A) = 0, then the regularity of A implies that A is a field, and conversely.

If A is a regular local ring and dim(A) = 1, then A is a discrete valuation ring. In fact, by theorem 4.1, $\mathfrak{m}$ is principal, and we can apply proposition 9 of B.C.A., VI, §3.

Finally, any ring A of power series in n variables $T_1, \ldots, T_n$ over a field is a regular local ring. This follows from the fact that $T_1, \ldots, T_n$ generate $\mathfrak{m}$ and form an A-regular sequence.

We globalize the notion of regular rings as follows:

Definition 4.2. A ring A is said to be regular if, for every maximal ideal $\mathfrak{m}$ of A, the local ring $A_{\mathfrak{m}}$ is regular.

We shall show later on that the polynomial ring in n variables over a field k is a regular ring.

Definition 4.3. Let A be a regular local ring. A set of generators of $\mathfrak{m}$ which forms an A-regular sequence is said to be a regular system of parameters of A.

Remark. Theorem 4.1 guarantees the existence of regular systems of parameters in any regular local ring A.

We also observe that, due to linguistical shortcomings, not every system of parameters of A which forms an A-regular sequence is necessarily a regular system of parameters, (see Definition 2.5) while every regular system of parameters is a system of parameters and an A-regular sequence.

We investigate the properties of regularity under quotient operations. We have

Proposition 4.1. Let A be a noetherian local ring, $x_i \in \mathfrak{m}$, $i = 1, \ldots, r$, $\mathfrak{J} = x_1 A + \ldots + x_r A$. The following three conditions are equivalent:

a) A is regular and $\{x_1, \ldots, x_r\}$ is contained in a regular system of parameters.

b) A is regular and the equivalence classes of $x_1, \ldots, x_r$

in $\mathfrak{m}/\mathfrak{m}^2$ are linearly independent

c) $\{x_1,\ldots,x_r\}$ is contained in a system of parameters, and $A/\mathfrak{J}$ is regular.

Furthermore the above three conditions imply that $\mathfrak{J}$ is prime.

Proof: a) $\Longleftrightarrow$ b). By Nakayama's lemma and the proof of theorem 4.1, any regular system of parameters gives rise to a k-basis of $\mathfrak{m}/\mathfrak{m}^2$ and conversely.

a) $\Longrightarrow$ c). Let $\mathfrak{n} = \mathfrak{m}\cdot A/\mathfrak{J}$, the maximal ideal of $A/\mathfrak{J}$. Consider the exact sequence

$$0 \to (\mathfrak{m}^2 + \mathfrak{J})/\mathfrak{m}^2 \to \mathfrak{m}/\mathfrak{m}^2 \to \mathfrak{n}/\mathfrak{n}^2 \to 0$$

(since we have the exact sequence $0 \to \mathfrak{m}^2 + \mathfrak{J} \to \mathfrak{m} \to \mathfrak{n}/\mathfrak{n}^2 \to 0$, we have $\mathfrak{m}/(\mathfrak{m}^2 + \mathfrak{J}) \simeq \mathfrak{n}/\mathfrak{n}^2$).

Let $n = \dim(A)$. Now, by a) and proposition 2.7 we have $\dim(A/\mathfrak{J}) = n - r$, and by b) (which has been shown to follow from a)) $\mathrm{rank}_k((\mathfrak{m}^2 + \mathfrak{J})/\mathfrak{m}^2) = r$ (since the equivalence classes of $x_1,\ldots,x_r$ in $(\mathfrak{m}^2 + \mathfrak{J})/\mathfrak{m}^2$ clearly generate it). Hence $\mathrm{rank}_k(\mathfrak{n}/\mathfrak{n}^2) = n - r = \dim(A/\mathfrak{J})$, and $A/\mathfrak{J}$ is regular. Hence c) is proved, since it is already assumed in a) that $\{x_1,\ldots,x_r\}$ is contained in a system of parameters.

c) $\Longrightarrow$ a). Since $A/\mathfrak{J}$ is regular, by proposition 2.7 and theorem 4.1 applied to $A/\mathfrak{J}$ we have

$$n - r = \dim(A/\mathfrak{J}) = \mathrm{rank}(\mathfrak{n}/\mathfrak{n}^2)$$

Since $x_1,\ldots,x_r$ generate $((\mathfrak{m}^2 + \mathfrak{J})/\mathfrak{m}^2)$ we have $\mathrm{rank}((\mathfrak{m}^2 + \mathfrak{J})/\mathfrak{m}^2) \leq r$. Hence $\mathrm{rank}(\mathfrak{m}/\mathfrak{m}^2) \leq n$. But rank($\mathfrak{m}/\mathfrak{m}^2$) $\geq$ n always, whence rank($\mathfrak{m}/\mathfrak{m}^2$) = n and A is regular.

Trivially, if $A/\mathfrak{J}$ is regular, $\mathfrak{J}$ is a prime ideal, since $A/\mathfrak{J}$ is an integral domain. The proposition is proved.

Corollary 4.2. Let A be a noetherian local ring, $t \in \mathfrak{m}$. Then the following conditions are equivalent:

a) A is regular, $t \notin \mathfrak{m}^2$

b) A/tA is regular and t does not belong to any minimal prime of A.

Proof: Apply propositions 4.1 and 3.1.

By proposition 4.1, we have that, if A is regular, and $\mathfrak{J}$ is generated by a subset of a regular system of parameters, then $A/\mathfrak{J}$ is regular. We sharpen this result in the following

Proposition 4.2. Let A be a noetherian regular local ring, $\mathfrak{J}$ an ideal of A. Then $A/\mathfrak{J}$ is regular if, and only if, $\mathfrak{J}$ is generated by a subset of a regular system of parameters.

Proof: The "if" part has been proved in proposition 4.1. Assume now that $A/\mathfrak{J}$ is regular, and let n = dim(A), n - r = dim($A/\mathfrak{J}$). Again we consider the exact sequence

$$0 \to ((\mathfrak{m}^2 + \mathfrak{J})/\mathfrak{m}^2) \to \mathfrak{m}/\mathfrak{m}^2 \to \mathfrak{n}/\mathfrak{n}^2 \to 0$$

where $\mathfrak{n}$ is as in the proof of proposition 4.1. We know that rank($\mathfrak{m}/\mathfrak{m}^2$) = n, and rank($\mathfrak{n}/\mathfrak{n}^2$) = n - r. Hence rank($(\mathfrak{m}^2 + \mathfrak{J})/\mathfrak{m}^2$) = r. Let $x_1, \ldots, x_r$ be elements of $\mathfrak{J}$ which are linearly independent mod $\mathfrak{m}^2$ and whose equivalence classes mod $\mathfrak{m}^2$ form a k-basis of $((\mathfrak{m}^2 + \mathfrak{J})/\mathfrak{m}^2)$. By extending the set of such equivalence classes to a k-basis of

$\mathfrak{m}/\mathfrak{m}^2$, and using theorem 4.1 we see that $\{x_1,\ldots,x_r\}$ is contained in a regular system of parameters. Let $\mathfrak{J}' = x_1 A + \ldots + x_r A$. Clearly $\mathfrak{J}' \subset \mathfrak{J}$. By proposition 4.1 $\mathfrak{J}'$ is a prime ideal and $\dim(A/\mathfrak{J}') = n - r$. But $\mathfrak{J}$ is also a prime ideal (since $A/\mathfrak{J}$ is regular) and we have $\dim(A/\mathfrak{J}) = \dim(A/\mathfrak{J}')$. The exact sequence

$$0 \to \mathfrak{J}/\mathfrak{J}' \to A/\mathfrak{J}' \to A/\mathfrak{J} \to 0$$

shows that $\mathfrak{J} = \mathfrak{J}'$ (otherwise $\mathfrak{J}\cdot A/\mathfrak{J}'$ is a non zero prime ideal of $A/\mathfrak{J}'$ and $\dim(A/\mathfrak{J}') > \dim(A/\mathfrak{J})$).

$\longleftrightarrow$

We now wish to show that, in the classical case, the notion of regularity we have given is equivalent to the classical one given in terms of the rank of a certain Jacobian.

We let $B = \mathbb{C}[X_1,\ldots,Y_n]$, $\mathfrak{a} \subset B$ an ideal, $\mathfrak{m} \supset \mathfrak{a}$ a maximal ideal, $A = B/\mathfrak{a}$. Then $\mathfrak{m}$ is generated by n linear polynomials of the form $X_i - \alpha_i$, $i = 1,\ldots,n$. Let $\mathfrak{a}$ be generated by the polynomials

$$P_\lambda,\ \lambda = 1,\ldots,t.$$

Let $\dim A_{\mathfrak{m}/\mathfrak{a}} = n - r$. We assert:

<u>Proposition 4.3</u>. $A_{\mathfrak{m}/\mathfrak{a}}$ is regular if, and only if, the rank of the matrix $(\frac{\partial P_\lambda}{\partial X_i}(\alpha_1,\ldots,\alpha_n))$ is r.

<u>Proof</u>: We have $A_{\mathfrak{m}/\mathfrak{a}} \cong B_\mathfrak{m}/\mathfrak{a}B_\mathfrak{m}$. By proposition 4.2 it follows that $A_{\mathfrak{m}/\mathfrak{a}}$ is regular, if, and only if, $\mathfrak{a}B_\mathfrak{m}$ is

generated by r elements, which can be imbedded in a $B_{\mathfrak{m}}$-regular system of parameters (since $B_{\mathfrak{m}}$ can be seen to be regular, $\mathfrak{m}B_{\mathfrak{m}}$ being generated by $\{X_1 - \alpha_1, \ldots, X_n - \alpha_n\}$). Furthermore we may assume that such r elements are actually in B, say $Q_1, \ldots, Q_r$. Since both sets $\{Q_1, \ldots, Q_r\}$ and $\{P_\lambda\}$ $\lambda = 1, \ldots, t$ generate $\mathfrak{a}B_{\mathfrak{m}}$ one easily sees that the ranks of the two matrices $((\frac{\partial Q_i}{\partial X_j}(\alpha_1, \ldots, \alpha_n)))$, $((\frac{\partial P_\lambda}{\partial X_j}(\alpha_1, \ldots, \alpha_n)))$ are equal.

Now, if $D: B_{\mathfrak{m}} \to B_{\mathfrak{m}}$ is any derivation, then clearly $D(\mathfrak{m}^2) \subset \mathfrak{m}$. Hence if φ denotes the composition

$$B_{\mathfrak{m}} \underset{D}{\to} B_{\mathfrak{m}} \to B_{\mathfrak{m}}/\mathfrak{m}B_{\mathfrak{m}} = \mathbb{C}$$

we have $\varphi(\mathfrak{m}^2) = 0$, and hence φ defines a $\mathbb{C}$-linear form

$$\tilde{\varphi}: \mathfrak{m}/\mathfrak{m}^2 \to \mathbb{C}$$

If $\varphi_j = \frac{\partial}{\partial X_j}$, $Q(X_1, \ldots, X_n) \in \mathfrak{m}$, then one immediately sees that $\tilde{\varphi}_j(Q) = \frac{\partial Q}{\partial X_j}(\alpha_1, \ldots, \alpha_n)$. Also it is clear that $\{\tilde{\varphi}_j\}$ $j = 1, \ldots, n$ is a set of n linearly independent forms over $\mathfrak{m}/\mathfrak{m}^2$. Since the equivalence classes of $Q_1, \ldots, Q_r$ in $\mathfrak{m}/\mathfrak{m}^2$ are linearly independent, it follows that rank $((\tilde{\varphi}_j(Q_i))) = r$, whence rank $((\frac{\partial P_\lambda}{\partial X_j}(\alpha_1, \ldots, \alpha_n))) = r$.

Conversely, if rank $((\frac{\partial P_\lambda}{\partial X_j}(\alpha_1, \ldots, \alpha_n))) = r$, then r of the P_λ's are linearly independent mod $\mathfrak{m}^2$, and by theorem 4.1 (since $B_{\mathfrak{m}}$ is regular of dimension n), they are a subset of a regular system of generators of $\mathfrak{m}$. Furthermore they generate $\mathfrak{a} + \mathfrak{m}^2/\mathfrak{m}^2$. Hence, by Nakayama's lemma, they generate $\mathfrak{a} B_{\mathfrak{m}}$ and we are done.

Classically, a point $(\alpha_1,\ldots,\alpha_n) \in \mathbb{C}^n$, belonging to the algebraic set defined by the ideal $\mathfrak{a}$ is called <u>simple</u> if the matrix $((\frac{\partial P}{\partial X_j}\lambda(\alpha_1,\ldots,\alpha_n)))$ has rank equal to $n - \dim(A_{\mathfrak{m}/\mathfrak{a}})$. Thus we have that <u>a point is simple if, and only if, its local ring is regular</u>.

We recall briefly the definition of a parametric representation of a variety, again in the classical case.

Let $\mathfrak{a} \subset \mathbb{C}[X_1,\ldots,X_n]$ be an ideal, and let V be the subset of $\mathbb{C}^n$ consisting of the common zeros of $\mathfrak{a}$. We say that V admits the parametric representation by polynomials

$$(*) \quad \begin{cases} X_1 = P_1(T_1,\ldots,T_m) \\ \cdots\cdots\cdots\cdots\cdots \\ X_n = P_n(T_1,\ldots,T_m) \end{cases}$$

if the homomorphism $\varphi: \mathbb{C}[X_1,\ldots,X_n] \to \mathbb{C}[T_1,\ldots,T_m]$ defined by $\varphi(X_i) = P_i(T_1,\ldots,T_m)$ has kernel $\mathfrak{a}$. Using the Hilbert Nullstellensatz one easily sees that this means that exactly all points of V are obtained by substituting some appropriate values for $T_1,\ldots,T_m$ in (*). Let now $\mathfrak{m} \subset \mathbb{C}[X_1,\ldots,X_n]$ be a maximal ideal with $\mathfrak{m} \supset \mathfrak{a}$, and let $\dim(A_{\mathfrak{m}/\mathfrak{a}}) = n - r$, where $A = \mathbb{C}[X_1,\ldots,X_n]/\mathfrak{a}$. Let $(\alpha_1,\ldots,\alpha_n)$ be the point of V corresponding to $\mathfrak{m}$, and let $\mathfrak{a}$ be generated by $\{Q_\lambda\}$ $1 \leqq \lambda \leqq t$. Let $(t_1,\ldots,t_m) \in \mathbb{C}^m$ such that $P_i(t_1,\ldots,t_m) = \alpha_i$. If the matrix $((\frac{\partial P}{\partial T_j}i(t_1,\ldots,t_m)))$ has rank $n - r$, then the homomorphism

$$\theta : \mathbb{C}dX_1 \oplus \ldots \oplus \mathbb{C}dX_n \to \mathbb{C}dT_1 \oplus \ldots \oplus \mathbb{C}dT_m$$

given by $\theta(\sum_{i=1}^{n} c_i \, dX_i) = \sum_{i=1}^{n} c_i \sum_{j=1}^{m} \frac{\partial P_i}{\partial T_j}(t_1,\ldots,t_m)\, dT_j$ has image of dimension $n - r$ and kernel generated by $\sum_{i=1}^{n} \frac{\partial Q_\lambda}{\partial X_i}(\alpha_1,\ldots,\alpha_n)\, dX_i$. Hence rank $(\frac{\partial Q_\lambda}{\partial X_i}(\alpha_1,\ldots,\alpha_n)) = r$, and $\{\alpha_1,\ldots,\alpha_n\}$ is a regular point of V. The example

$$\begin{cases} X = T^2 \\ Y = T^2 \\ Z = T^2 \end{cases}$$

where $n = 3$, $r = 2$, easily show (take $X = Y = Z = T = 0$) that the converse of the above statement is false. (In fact here V is the line $X = Y = Z$, and proposition 4.1 shows that the origin is a simple point on such line, while rank $((0,0,0)) = 0$).

<u>Remark</u>. The concept of regularity enables us to solve the problem of distinguishing the local ring of the three examples given in the introduction. In fact, while the third local ring is regular, the first two are not (apply Proposition 4.3).

We introduce one last numerical notion to be attached to a local ring.

<u>Definition 4.4</u>. Let A be a ring, M an A-module. A <u>projective resolution of M</u> of length n is an exact sequence

$$0 \to L_n \to L_{n-1} \to \ldots \to L_1 \to L_0 \to M \to 0$$

where L_i is a projective A-module, $i = 0,\ldots,n$.

Definition 4.5. Let M be an A-module. Then the projective dimension of M, dim. proj. (M) is defined as the infimum of the lengths of all projective resolutions of M. The cohomological dimension of A, coh. dim(A), is defined as the supremum of the projective dimensions of all A-modules.

We state, without proof, two of the fundamental theorems concerning the notion of coh. dim(A). The proofs involve tools whose introduction would take us far afield, and of which we shall have no need in the remaining part of this work.

Theorem 4.2. (Hilbert-Serre) Let A be a noetherian local ring. Then one (and only one) of the following two alternatives hold

1) coh. dim(A) = ∞

2) A is regular and coh. dim(A) = dim(A)

Corollary 4.3. If A is a noetherian regular local ring, and $\mathfrak{p} \in \operatorname{Spec}(A)$, then $A_{\mathfrak{p}}$ is regular.

Proof: The homomorphism $A \to A_{\mathfrak{p}}$ shows that every $A_{\mathfrak{p}}$-module is an A-module. Now, for noetherian local rings the notions of projective and flat modules are equivalent. Since $A_{\mathfrak{p}}$ is A-flat, if L is $A_{\mathfrak{p}}$-flat and

$$0 \to M \to N$$

is an exact sequence of A-modules, we have

$$0 \to A_{\mathfrak{p}} \otimes_A M \to A_{\mathfrak{p}} \otimes_A N \text{ is exact}$$

and

$$0 \to L \otimes_{A_{\mathfrak{p}}} (A_{\mathfrak{p}} \otimes_A M) \to L \otimes_{A_{\mathfrak{p}}} (A_{\mathfrak{p}} \otimes_A N) \quad \text{is exact}$$

or

$$0 \to L \otimes_A M \to L \otimes_A N \quad \text{is exact,}$$

and L is A-flat. Hence every projective resolution of an $A_{\mathfrak{p}}$-module M is a projective resolution of the A-module M, and we obtain the following inequality

$$\text{coh dim}(A_{\mathfrak{p}}) \leq \text{coh dim}(A)$$

from which the corollary follows immediately via Theorem 4.2.

Theorem 4.3. (Auslander-Buchsbaum) Every noetherian regular local ring is a unique factorization domain.

For the proofs of Theorems 4.2 and 4.3 we refer the reader to A. Grothendieck's "Elements de Geometrie Algebrique", Chapter 0_{IV} (The portion of Chapter 0 preceding Chapter IV), section 17.3, and Chapter IV, section 21.11.

The problem of classifying all regular local rings is at the moment unsolved, and probably unsolvable as stated. In fact, if X, Y, are two irreducible schemes and $\varphi: X \to Y$ a morphism such that, for some $x \in X$, $\mathcal{O}_{x,X} \simeq \mathcal{O}_{\varphi(x),Y}$ and both are regular, then, under certain appropriate finiteness conditions, φ is birational. Hence to classify regular local rings requires first a classification of birationally equivalent schemes, a very tall order at the moment.

We complete this section with some results concerning the two notions of depth and regularity.

We call a noetherian ring A normal if A is the direct sum of integrally closed integral domains, and reduced if its nilradical is 0.

Definition 4.6. Let A be a noetherian ring, k a non-negative integer.

1) We say that A satisfies condition (S_k) if, for every $\mathfrak{p} \in \mathrm{Spec}(A)$

$$\mathrm{depth}(A_{\mathfrak{p}}) \geqq \min[k, \dim(A_{\mathfrak{p}})]$$

2) We say that A satisfies condition (R_k) if, for every $\mathfrak{p} \in \mathrm{Spec}(A)$

$$\dim A_{\mathfrak{p}} \leqq k \text{ implies } A_{\mathfrak{p}} \text{ is regular.}$$

Corollary 4.4. a) S_o always holds:

b) A satisfies (S_k) if, and only if, for every $\mathfrak{p} \in \mathrm{Spec}(A)$, depth $A_{\mathfrak{p}} \geqq k$ and, if $\dim(A_{\mathfrak{p}}) \leqq k$, then $A_{\mathfrak{p}}$ is C-M.

Proof: a) is obvious. To prove b) we recall that $\mathrm{depth}(A_{\mathfrak{p}}) \leq \dim(A_{\mathfrak{p}})$. Therefore, if $k < \dim(A_{\mathfrak{p}})$, $\mathrm{depth}(A_{\mathfrak{p}}) \geqq k$ is equivalent to the requirement of (S_k), and if $k \geqq \dim(A_{\mathfrak{p}})$, then $\mathrm{depth}(A_{\mathfrak{p}}) = \dim(A_{\mathfrak{p}})$ (i.e. $A_{\mathfrak{p}}$ is C-M) is again equivalent to the requirement of (S_k).

Proposition 4.4. (S_k) is equivalent to the following condition: For every $t \in A$ and every A_t-regular sequence $\{x_1,\ldots,x_r\}$, $r < k$, the A_t-module $A_t/x_1A_t + \ldots + x_rA_t$ has no immersed primes.

Proof: $k = 1$, whence $r = 0$. We will show that S_1 is equivalent to saying that A has no immersed primes. Let $\mathfrak{p}$ be a prime of A which is not minimal. Then $\dim(A_{\mathfrak{p}}) \geqq 1$, whence by (S_1) $\mathrm{depth}(A_{\mathfrak{p}}) \geqq 1$.

Hence $\mathfrak{p} \notin \mathrm{Ass}(A)$ (if $\mathfrak{p}$ is the annihilator of $a \in A$, then $\frac{a}{1} \neq 0$ in $A_{\mathfrak{p}}$ and $\mathfrak{p}A_{\mathfrak{p}}$ is the annihilator of it).

Conversely, if A has no immersed primes, let $\mathfrak{p} \in \mathrm{Spec}(A)$.

If $\mathfrak{p} \in \mathrm{Ass}(A)$, then $\mathfrak{p}$ is minimal, hence $\min[1, \dim A_{\mathfrak{p}}] = 0$ and $\mathrm{depth}(A_{\mathfrak{p}}) \geqq 0$. If $\mathfrak{p} \notin \mathrm{Ass}\, A$, then $\mathfrak{p}$ is not minimal and $\min[1, \dim A_{\mathfrak{p}}] = 1$. If $\mathrm{depth}(A_{\mathfrak{p}}) = 0$, then by theorem 3.1, $\mathfrak{p}A_{\mathfrak{p}} \in \mathrm{Ass}(A_{\mathfrak{p}})$ whence $\mathfrak{p} \in \mathrm{Ass}(A)$, a contradiction. Hence A satisfies (S_1).

We proceed by induction on k. Let $k > 1$.

Let A satisfy (S_k), and let $\{x_1,\dots,x_r\}$, $r < k$ be an A_t-regular sequence. Let $B = A_t/x_1A_t$. From proposition 3.1 and theorem 3.1 we see that B satisfies (S_{k-1}) (since, for every $\mathfrak{p} \in \mathrm{Spec}(A_t)$ with $x_1 \in \mathfrak{p}$, x_1 is $A_{\mathfrak{p}}$-regular) hence $B/x_2 B +\dots+ x_r B = A_t/x_1A_t +\dots+ x_rA_t$ has no imbedded primes.
Conversely, assume that for $t \in A$, the A_t-module $A_t/x_1A_t+\dots+x_rA_t$ has no immersed primes, for every A_t-regular sequence $\{x_1,\dots,x_r\}$ with $r < k$.

By the induction assumption, A satisfies (S_{k-1}). Let $\mathfrak{p} \in \mathrm{Spec}(A)$. We proceed in steps.

<u>Case 1</u>. $\dim(A_{\mathfrak{p}}) = r < k$. Since A satisfies (S_{k-1}) we have

$$\mathrm{depth}(A_{\mathfrak{p}}) \geqq \min(k-1, r) = r$$

whence $\mathrm{depth}(A_{\mathfrak{p}}) \geqq \min(k, \dim(A_{\mathfrak{p}}))$.

<u>Case 2</u>. $\dim(A_{\mathfrak{p}}) = r \geqq k$. Again, since A satisfies (S_{k-1}) we have $\mathrm{depth}(A_{\mathfrak{p}}) \geqq \min(k-1, r) = k - 1$. Hence there exists a sequence $x_1,\dots,x_{k-1} \in \mathfrak{p}A_{\mathfrak{p}}$ which is $A_{\mathfrak{p}}$-regular, and we may assume $x_i \in \mathfrak{p}$. Then $x_1,\dots,x_{k-1}$ is an A_t-regular sequence for some $t \notin \mathfrak{p}$. Therefore, by assumption
$B_t = A_t/x_1A_t +\dots+ x_{k-1} A_t$ has no immersed primes. Since

$\dim(B_{\mathfrak{p}B}) = \dim(A_{\mathfrak{p}}/x_1 A_{\mathfrak{p}} + \ldots + x_{k-1} A_{\mathfrak{p}}) = \dim(A_{\mathfrak{p}}) - (k-1) \geqq 1$,
and B_t has no immersed primes, it follows that $\mathfrak{p} \notin \mathrm{Ass}(B_t)$. Hence $\mathrm{depth}(B_{\mathfrak{p}}) \geqq 1$. We then obtain

$$1 \leqq \mathrm{depth}(A_{\mathfrak{p}}/x_1 A_{\mathfrak{p}} + \ldots + x_{k-1} A_{\mathfrak{p}}) = \mathrm{depth}(A_{\mathfrak{p}}) - (k-1)$$

whence $\mathrm{depth}(A_{\mathfrak{p}}) \geqq k$, and (S_k) is proved.

We are now in the position of obtaining two criterions for A to be normal, and reduced respectively.

Proposition 4.5. A is reduced if, and only if, A satisfies both (S_1) and (R_0).

Proof: We observe that clearly (R_0) is equivalent to saying that, for all minimal primes $\mathfrak{p}$ of A, (whence $\dim(A_{\mathfrak{p}}) = 0$) $A_{\mathfrak{p}}$ is a field.

Now assume that A is reduced. Then, if $\mathfrak{p}$ is a minimal prime of A, $\mathfrak{p} A_{\mathfrak{p}} = (0)$ (since $0 = \bigcap_{\substack{\mathfrak{q} \subset A \\ \mathfrak{q} \text{ minimal}}} \mathfrak{q}$, and $\mathfrak{q} A_{\mathfrak{p}} = 0$ for $\mathfrak{q} \neq \mathfrak{p}$ and minimal), whence $A_{\mathfrak{p}}$ is a field and (R_0) follows. To prove that A satisifes (S_1) we proceed by contradiction. If A does not satisfy (S_1) then, by proposition 4.4, there exists a prime $\mathfrak{q} \in \mathrm{Ass}(A)$ which is not minimal. Let $\mathfrak{p}_1, \mathfrak{p}_2, \ldots, \mathfrak{p}_k$ be the minimal primes of A. Then $\mathfrak{q} \not\subset \bigcup_{i=1}^{k} \mathfrak{p}_i$, (since $\mathfrak{q}$ is not minimal) whence there exists $x \in \mathfrak{q}$, $x \notin \bigcup_{i=1} \mathfrak{p}_i$. Since $x \in \mathfrak{q} \in \mathrm{Ass}(A)$, x is a zero divisor in A. Let x_i be the image of x under $A \xrightarrow{\varphi_i} A_{\mathfrak{p}_i}$ $i = 1, \ldots, k$. We have $xt = 0$ for some non zero t. Then $x_i \varphi_i(t) = 0$. Since

$x \notin \mathfrak{p}_i$, x_i is a unit in $A_{\mathfrak{p}_i}$, whence $\varphi_i(t) = 0$, $i = 1,\dots,k$. Then (by the definition of $A_{\mathfrak{p}_i}$) $t \in \mathfrak{p}_i$, $i = 1,\dots,k$. Since A is reduced, $\bigcap_{i=1}^{k} \mathfrak{p}_i = 0$, whence $t = 0$ a contradiction.

Assume, conversely, that A satisfies both (S_1) and (R_o). Let $\mathfrak{p}_1,\dots,\mathfrak{p}_k$ be again the minimal prime ideals of A. We wish to show that A is reduced, i.e. that $\bigcap_{i=1}^{k} \mathfrak{p}_i = 0$. Assume that there exists a non zero $z \in \bigcap_{i=1}^{k} \mathfrak{p}_i$. By (R_o), $A_{\mathfrak{p}_i}$ is a field, whence $\mathfrak{p}_i A_{\mathfrak{p}_i} = 0$, $i = 1,\dots,k$, whence $\varphi_i(z) = 0$, $i = 1,\dots,k$. Therefore, for every i, there exists $s_i \notin \mathfrak{p}_i$ such that $s_i \cdot z = 0$, i.e. $\operatorname{ann}(z) \not\subset \mathfrak{p}_i$, $i = 1,\dots,k$, whence $\operatorname{ann}(z) \not\subset \bigcup_{i=1}^{k} \mathfrak{p}_i$. By (S_1), since A has no imbedded primes, $\bigcup_{i=1}^{k} \mathfrak{p}_i = \bigcup_{\mathfrak{p} \in \operatorname{Ass}(A)} \mathfrak{p}$ = the set of zero divisors of A. We have that, for a $z \neq 0$, there exists a non zero divisor of A which annihilates z, clearly a contradiction, Q.E.D.

<u>Proposition 4.6</u>. (Serre) Let A be noetherian. Then A is normal if, and only if, A satisfies both (S_2) and (R_1).

<u>Proof</u>: We remark first of all that A satisfies both (S_2) and (R_1) if, and only if, the following holds:

(*) Let $\mathfrak{p} \in \operatorname{Spec}(A)$. If $\dim(A_{\mathfrak{p}}) \leqq 1$, then $A_{\mathfrak{p}}$ is regular. If $\dim A_{\mathfrak{p}} \geqq 2$, then $\operatorname{depth}(A_{\mathfrak{p}}) \geqq 2$.

We leave the verification of our remark to the reader.

Now, if A is normal, so is $A_{\mathfrak{p}}$. Hence, if $\dim(A_{\mathfrak{p}}) \leqq 1$, then $A_{\mathfrak{p}}$ is either a field (which is regular) or, by the discussion on page 38, a valuation ring, hence by proposition 9 in B.C.A., VI, §3, no. 6, A is a discrete valuation ring. Hence $A_{\mathfrak{p}}$ is regular, and (R_1) is satisfied.

To prove that (S_2) is satisfied we have to prove, in addition to the above, that $\operatorname{depth}(A_{\mathfrak{p}}) \geqq 2$ when $\dim(A_{\mathfrak{p}}) \geqq 2$. This was proved during the proof of remark 3) after definition 3.3.

Assume now that (*) above is satisfied. We remark first of all that, trivially (R_k) implies (R_{k-j}), $j = 0,\ldots,k$, and also that (S_k) implies (S_{k-j}), $j = 0,\ldots,k$. Hence, since (S_2) and (R_1) hold, so do (S_1) and (R_o), and A is reduced by proposition 4.5.

Let $\{\mathfrak{p}_i\}_{i\in I}$ be the minimal primes of A. Note that I is finite and that, since A is reduced $\bigcap_{i\in I} \mathfrak{p}_i = (0)$. Let K_i be the field of fractions of $A/\mathfrak{p}_i$, and let $R = \prod_{i\in I} K_i$. Then the canonical homomorphism $A \to R$ is an injection. Identifying A with its image, we see that we have to prove that A is integrally closed in R. Let $h \in R$ be integral over A. Since R is the total ring of fractions of A, $h = f/g$ for some $f, g \in A$, g is not a zero divisor of A.

From an equation of integral dependence of h over A we get, by multiplication by an appropriate power of g

$$(*) \qquad f^n + \sum_j a_j f^{n-j} g^j = 0 \qquad a_j \in A$$

Let $\mathfrak{p} \in \operatorname{Spec}(A)$ be such that $\dim(A_{\mathfrak{p}}) = 1$
By (R_1) $A_{\mathfrak{p}}$ is regular, whence, by corollary 4.1, it is

integrally closed. Let $f_{\mathfrak{p}}$, $g_{\mathfrak{p}}$ denote the images of f, g under $A \to A_{\mathfrak{p}}$. Note that $g_{\mathfrak{p}}$ is not a zero divisor in $A_{\mathfrak{p}}$, hence $f_{\mathfrak{p}}/g_{\mathfrak{p}}$ belongs to the field of fractions of $A_{\mathfrak{p}}$. From (*) above, first localizing at $\mathfrak{p}$ and then dividing by $g_{\mathfrak{p}}^n$ we see that $f_{\mathfrak{p}}/g_{\mathfrak{p}}$ is integral over $A_{\mathfrak{p}}$, hence $f_{\mathfrak{p}}/g_{\mathfrak{p}} \in A_{\mathfrak{p}}$ and $f_{\mathfrak{p}} A_{\mathfrak{p}} \subset g_{\mathfrak{p}} A_{\mathfrak{p}}$, whence $(fA)_{\mathfrak{p}} \subset (gA)_{\mathfrak{p}}$. Now, since g is not a zero divisor of A, g is A-regular and, by proposition 4.4, A/gA has no immersed primes containing gA. If $\mathfrak{q}_1, \ldots, \mathfrak{q}_r$ denote the minimal primes of A/gA, by the Hauptidealsatz we have $\dim A_{\mathfrak{q}_j} = 1$, and by the previous discussion $(fA)_{\mathfrak{q}_j} \subset (gA)_{\mathfrak{q}_j}$. Let $\mu_j : A \to A_{\mathfrak{q}_j}$ be the canonical homomorphisms. Let $gA = \bigcap_j \mathfrak{q}'_j$ be a primary irredundant decomposition of gA in A. Then $\{\mathfrak{q}_j\} = \mathrm{Ass}(A/\mathfrak{q}'_j)$ and the $\mathfrak{q}_j$ are minimal in Ass(A/gA), j = 1,...,r. Then, by proposition 5 of B.C.A., 4, §2, no. 3, we have $\mathfrak{q}'_j = \mu_j^{-1}[(gA)_{\mathfrak{q}_j}]$, i.e. $gA = \bigcap_j \mu_j^{-1}[(gA)_{\mathfrak{q}_j}]$. Clearly $fA \subset \bigcap_j \mu_j^{-1}[(fA)_{\mathfrak{q}_j}]$, whence, by $(fA)_{\mathfrak{q}_j} \subset (gA)_{\mathfrak{q}_j}$, $fA \subset gA$, i.e. $h = f/g \in A$, Q.E.D.

<——————>

We end this section with a few examples from classical Algebraic Geometry. Let $A = \mathbb{C}[X_1, \ldots, X_n]/\mathfrak{a}$ be reduced (whence (R_o) and (S_1) hold). In this case the geometrical interpretation of the fact that R_1 holds for A is that the local ring of the generic point of any irreducible subvariety of codimension 1 of Spec(A) is regular, hence a valuation ring. If R_1 does <u>not</u> hold, then there exists a prime $\mathfrak{p} \in \mathrm{Spec}(A)$ such that $\dim(A_{\mathfrak{p}}) = 1$ and $A_{\mathfrak{p}}$ is not regular. In this case $V(\mathfrak{p})$ consists entirely of singular points, i.e. points whose local rings are not regular. To see this let $\mathfrak{q} \in V(\mathfrak{p})$ and assume $A_{\mathfrak{q}}$ is regular. We have $\mathfrak{q} \supset \mathfrak{p}$, whence $A_{\mathfrak{p}} \simeq (A_{\mathfrak{q}})_{\mathfrak{p}A_{\mathfrak{q}}}$. If $A_{\mathfrak{q}}$ is regular, it follows from corollary 4.3 that $A_{\mathfrak{p}}$ is regular, contrary to assumption. In particular, all closed points $\mathfrak{m}$ of $V(\mathfrak{p})$ must be singular, and the problem of determining whether A satisfies (R_1) or not is reduced, via proposition 4.3, to the examination of the rank of the Jacobian of a set of generators of $\mathfrak{a}$.

We illustrate the above by studying the following example: Let

$$\begin{cases} T_0 = X^4 \\ T_1 = X^3Y \\ T_2 = X^2Y^2 \\ T_3 = XY^3 \\ T_4 = Y^4 \end{cases}$$

be the parametric representation of a <u>cone</u> in five dimensional affine space, i.e. we consider the inclusion

$$\mathbb{C}[X^4,\ X^3Y,\ X^2Y^2,\ XY^3,\ Y^4] \to \mathbb{C}[X,\ Y].$$

Let V denote such a cone. The ideal of V is the kernel $\mathfrak{a}$ of the homomorphism $\varphi : \mathbb{C}[T_0, T_1, \ldots, T_4] \to \mathbb{C}[X, Y]$ given by $\varphi(T_i) = X^{4-i}\,Y^i$.

It is a rewarding exercise for the reader to check that $\mathfrak{a}$ is generated by $(T_0 T_2 - T_1^2)$, $(T_1 T_3 - T_2^2)$, $(T_2 T_4 - T_3^2)$, and that V is a two-dimensional cone. The discussion after proposition 4.3 tells us that the origin is the only possible singular point of V. whence (R_1) holds for

$\mathbb{C}[T_0,T_1,T_2,T_3,T_4]/\mathfrak{a} \simeq \mathbb{C}[X^4,X^3Y,X^2Y^2,XY^3,Y^4]$.

To see that (S_2) also holds, we need only check that the depth of the local ring of every closed point of V is 2. This is clear for non singular points, since the local ring is then regular, and it is also true at the origin, since X^4, $Y^4 \in \mathbb{C}[X^4,X^3Y,X^2Y^2,XY^3,Y^4]$ is a $\mathbb{C}[X^4,X^3Y,X^2Y^2,XY^3,Y^4]_{\mathfrak{m}}$ - regular sequence, where $\mathfrak{m}$ denotes the maximal ideal generated by X^4,X^3Y,X^2Y^2,XY^3,Y^4.

Consider now $A = \mathbb{C}[X^4,X^3Y,XY^3,Y^4] \subset \mathbb{C}[X,Y]$. Here Spec A is a two dimensional cone in 4-dimensional space, and the discussion after proposition 4.3 tells us that the origin is the only possible singular point of Spec(A). Hence (R_1) holds for A.

Now $(X^2Y^2)^2 = X^4Y^4$ shows that X^2Y^2 is integral over A. However one easily checks $X^2Y^2 \notin A$, whence A is not integrally closed, and (S_2) does not hold for A. Note that this implies $\operatorname{depth}(A_{\mathfrak{m}}) \leq 1$, where $\mathfrak{m}$ denotes the maximal ideal of the origin in Spec(A).

Finally consider $A = \mathbb{C}[X^4,X^3Y,X^3Y,XY^3,Y^4,Z] \subset \mathbb{C}[X,Y,Z]$. Here Spec(A) is a three dimensional variety in five dimensional space, and, again by the discussion after proposition 4.3, (R_1) holds for A.

If $\mathfrak{p} \in \operatorname{Spec}(A)$ and $\dim(A_{\mathfrak{p}}) = 2$, then $\operatorname{Spec}(A/\mathfrak{p}) \neq \{\mathfrak{m}_a\}$ where $\mathfrak{m}_a$ denotes the maximal ideal of the point (0, 0, a). Hence $A_{\mathfrak{p}}$ is regular and $\operatorname{depth}(A_{\mathfrak{p}}) = 2$.

If $\dim(A_{\mathfrak{p}}) = 3$, and $\mathfrak{p} \neq \mathfrak{m}_a$, then $A_{\mathfrak{p}}$ is again regular and $\operatorname{depth}(A_{\mathfrak{p}}) = 3$. At $\mathfrak{m}_a$ we have $\dim(A_{\mathfrak{m}_a}) = 3$, and $\operatorname{depth}(A_{\mathfrak{m}_a}) \geq 2$, since clearly Y^4, $Z - a$ form an $A_{\mathfrak{m}_a}$-regular sequence. Hence (S_2) holds for A.

Actually $\operatorname{depth}(A_{\mathfrak{m}_a}) = 2$, which gives us an example of a local integral domain which is not a C-M ring, whence A itself is not a C-M ring.

That $\operatorname{depth}(A_{\mathfrak{m}_a}) = 2$ is proved as follows. One can take n=0. Let $A' = \mathbb{C}[X^4, X^3Y, XY^3, Y^4]$. Then $A/ZA \simeq A'$. Let $\mathfrak{m}'$ be the maximal ideal of A' corresponding to the origin of Spec(A'). We know from above that $\operatorname{depth}(A'_{\mathfrak{m}'}) \leq 1$, and $\operatorname{depth}(A_{\mathfrak{m}_0}) \geq 2$. Furthermore we have

$$A'_{\mathfrak{m}'} = A_{\mathfrak{m}_0}/ZA_{\mathfrak{m}_0}$$

and since Z is $A_{\mathfrak{m}_0}$-regular, $1 \geq \operatorname{depth}(A'_{\mathfrak{m}'}) = \operatorname{depth}(A_{\mathfrak{m}_0}) - 1$, whence $\operatorname{depth}(A_{\mathfrak{m}_0}) \leq 2$. We are done.

It is a rewarding exercise for the reader to check that the kernel $\mathfrak{a}$ of the homomorphism $\varphi: \mathbb{C}[T_1, T_2, T_3, T_4] \to \mathbb{C}[X^4, X^3Y, XY^3, Y^4]$ - defined by $\varphi(T_1) = X^4$, $\varphi(T_2) = X^3Y$, $\varphi(T_3) = XY^3$, $\varphi(T_4) = Y^4$ is generated by $T_1^2 T_3 - T_2^3$, $T_2 T_4^2 - T_3^3$, T_1, $T_4^3 - T_3^4$, and that no two of the above three polynomials generate $\mathfrak{a}$.

§5. BEHAVIOR UNDER LOCAL HOMOMORPHISM

In this section we let A, B be local rings, unless otherwise specified, with unique maximal ideals $\mathfrak{m}$, $\mathfrak{n}$ respectively.

We recall that a homomorphism $\varphi: A \to B$ is called <u>local</u> if

$\varphi(\mathfrak{m}) \subset \mathfrak{n}$, or equivalently, $\varphi^{-1}(\mathfrak{n}) = \mathfrak{m}$. Geometrically this means that, in the associated continuous map ${}^a\varphi:\mathrm{Spec}(B) \to \mathrm{Spec}(A)$, the unique closed point of Spec(B) maps into the unique closed point of Spec(A).

As an example of a non local homomorphism we consider the inclusion of an integral local ring A into its field of fraction B. Here the unique closed point (in fact the only point) of Spec(B) maps into the generic point of Spec(A), as far from the closed point as one can get!

5A. We study here the behavior of dimension under a local homomorphism.

Let $\varphi:A \to B$ be a local homomorphism, and let $X = \mathrm{Spec}(B)$, $Y = \mathrm{Spec}(A)$, whence ${}^a\varphi:X \to Y$. Let ${}^a\varphi = f$. The inverse image $f^{-1}(y)$ of the unique closed point y of Y contains the unique closed point x of X, and perhaps something more. In any event, $f^{-1}(y)$ consists of all those prime ideals $\mathfrak{p}$ of B such that $\varphi^{-1}(\mathfrak{p}) = \mathfrak{m}$, i.e. those prime ideals which contain $\mathfrak{m}B$ (we consider B as an algebra over $\varphi(A)$, and write $\mathfrak{m}$ for $\varphi(\mathfrak{m})$). So $f^{-1}(y)$ consists of the prime ideals of the ring $B/\mathfrak{m}B = A/\mathfrak{m} \otimes_A B$. We have shown $f^{-1}(y) = \mathrm{Spec}(B/\mathfrak{m}B)$. In the sequel we shall denote by k the residue field $A/\mathfrak{m}$.

Optimally one would hope that $\dim X - \dim(f^{-1}(y)) = \dim Y$. However, as we shall see, this is not always true. We begin examining the situation with the following

Proposition 5.1. $\dim(B) \leq \dim(A) + \dim(k \otimes_A B)$

Proof: Note that, with the identification $k \otimes_A B = B/\mathfrak{m}B$ one easily sees that $k \otimes_A B$ is a local ring with maximal ideal

$\mathfrak{n}B/\mathfrak{m}B$. Hence $\dim(k \otimes_A B) < +\infty$.

Let $\dim(A) = m$, and let $s_1,\ldots,s_m$ be a system of parameters of A. Let $\mathfrak{a} = s_1 A +\ldots+ s_m A$. By definition $A/\mathfrak{a}$ is artinian, whence $\mathfrak{m}/\mathfrak{a}$ is nilpotent in $A/\mathfrak{a}$, i.e. a sufficiently high power of every element of $\mathfrak{m}$ is in $\mathfrak{a}$. Since an element of $\mathfrak{m}B$ is a linear combination of a finite number of elements of $\mathfrak{m}$ with coefficients in B, a sufficiently high power of every element of $\mathfrak{m}B$ is in $\mathfrak{a}B$, i.e. $\mathfrak{m}B/\mathfrak{a}B$ is nilpotent in $B/\mathfrak{a}B$. The nil-radical $\mathfrak{r}$ of $B/\mathfrak{a}B$ contains $\mathfrak{m}B/\mathfrak{a}B$, whence

$$\dim(B/\mathfrak{m}B) = \dim([B/\mathfrak{a}B]/(\mathfrak{m}B/\mathfrak{a}B)) =$$

$$\dim[(B/\mathfrak{a}B)/\mathfrak{r}] = \dim(B/\mathfrak{a}B)$$

clearly $B/\mathfrak{a}B = B/s_1 B +\ldots+ s_m B$. Let $\dim(B/\mathfrak{a}B) = n$, and let $\bar{t}_1,\ldots,\bar{t}_n$ be a system of parameters of $B/\mathfrak{a}B$. Let $t_i \in B$, $i = 1,\ldots,n$ be such that $\bar{t}_i = t_i + \mathfrak{a}B$. We have that $C = (B/\mathfrak{a}B)/\bar{t}_1(B/\mathfrak{a}B) +\ldots+ \bar{t}_n(B/\mathfrak{a}B)$ is artinian, and clearly $C = B/(t_1 B +\ldots+ t_n B + s_1 B +\ldots+ s_m B)$, i.e. $t_1,\ldots,t_n$, $\varphi(s_1),\ldots,\varphi(s_m)$ generate an ideal primary for $\mathfrak{n}$. Then $\dim(B) = s(B) \leq m + n$, and the proposition is proved, since $n = \dim(B/\mathfrak{a}B) = \dim(B/\mathfrak{m}B)$.

<u>Remark</u>. It is possible that inequality hold in the statement of proposition 5.1. In fact one can take $B = A/\mathfrak{m} = k$, where $\dim(A) \geq 1$. A more difficult example can be given, where $\dim(A) = 2$, $B = C_{\mathfrak{m}A}$ where C is a finite algebra over A and $\dim(B) = 1$. Clearly $1 < 2$, whence the inequality.

As a consequence of Theorem 5.1 below we shall see that, when B is A-flat, equality in proposition 5.1 does hold.

Flatness, however, is a stronger requirement than needed. In fact, the conclusion of the following lemma is sufficient, as we shall see, to guarantee equality in proposition 5.1.

Lemma 5.1. Let $\varphi: A \to B$ be a homomorphism of (not necessarily local or noetherian) rings and let B be A-flat. Let $X = \mathrm{Spec}(B)$, $Y = \mathrm{Spec}(A)$, ${}^a\varphi: X \to Y$. Let V be an irreducible closed subset of Y. Then the generic points of all the irreducible components of ${}^a\varphi^{-1}(V)$ are mapped into the generic point of V.

Proof: Let $V = \mathrm{Spec}(A/\mathfrak{p})$, where $\mathfrak{p}$ denotes the generic point of V. Let ${}^a\varphi = f$. Then $f^{-1}(V) = \mathrm{Spec}(B/\mathfrak{p}B) = \mathrm{Spec}(A/\mathfrak{p} \otimes_A B)$. Since B is A-flat, $B/\mathfrak{p}B$ is $A/\mathfrak{p}$-flat. In fact, if

$$0 \to M \to N$$

is an exact sequence of $A/\mathfrak{p}$-modules, it is also an exact sequence of A-modules and, since B is A-flat

$$0 \to M \otimes_A B \to N \otimes_A B \text{ is exact.}$$

But

$$M \otimes_A B = M \otimes_{A/\mathfrak{p}} (A/\mathfrak{p} \otimes_A B)$$

$$N \otimes_A B = N \otimes_{A/\mathfrak{p}} (A/\mathfrak{p} \otimes_A B)$$

whence $(A/\mathfrak{p}) \otimes_A B$ is $A/\mathfrak{p}$-flat. The homomorphism φ induces a canonical homomorphism $A/\mathfrak{p} \to B/\mathfrak{p}B$, i.e. we may assume $V = Y$, and hence $f^{-1}(V) = X$. We denote by O_X and O_Y the sheaves of local rings of X and Y respectively. (See the introduction)

Let T be an irreducible component of X, with x as generic point. Let $f(x) = y$. We have to show that y is the generic point of Y. Since flatness is preserved under localization, O_x is O_y-flat. In fact it is faithfully flat, i.e. $\mathfrak{m}_y \cdot O_x \neq O_x$ where $\mathfrak{m}_y$ denotes the unique maximal ideal of O_y. To see this we observe that, if $\mathfrak{m}_y \cdot O_x = O_x$ then, by Nakayama's lemma $O_x = 0$, a contradiction. Since O_x is faithfully flat over O_y, by proposition 8 of B.C.A., I, §3, no. 5, we have that the homomorphism $\tilde{\varphi}_x : O_y \to O_x$ is injective, and that $\mathrm{Spec}(O_x) \to \mathrm{Spec}(O_y)$ is surjective. Let y' be the generic point of Y. Then $j_{y'} \subset j_y$, whence $j_{y'} \cdot O_y \in \mathrm{Spec}(O_y)$ and there exists a prime ideal $\mathfrak{p} \in \mathrm{Spec}(O_x)$ such that $\tilde{\varphi}_x^{-1}(\mathfrak{p}) = j_{y'} \cdot O_y$. $O_x = B_{j_x}$ and j_x is minimal, whence $\mathfrak{p} = j_x \cdot O_x$. Then $y' = y$,

Q.E.D.

Note. Lemma 5.1 shows that the projection indicated in the figure is not a flat morphism.

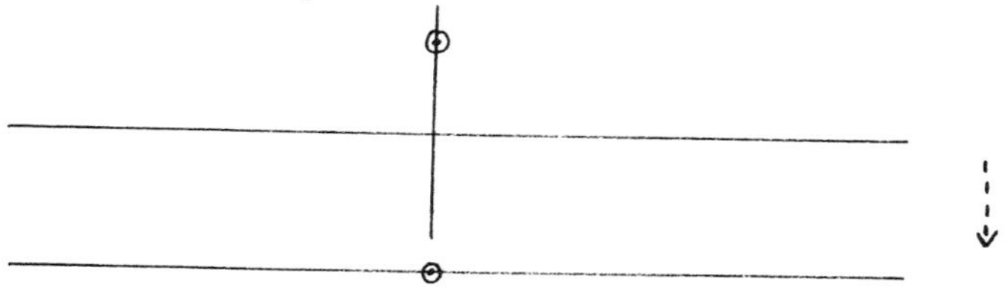

We return now to discussing when equality holds in Proposition 5.1.

Theorem 5.1. Let A, B be local, noetherian rings, $\varphi : A \to B$ be a local homomorphism, $X = \mathrm{Spec}(B)$, $Y = \mathrm{Spec}(A)$, ${}^a\varphi : X \to Y$ the associated morphism. We assume the following condition:

(*) For every closed irreducible subset V of Y, $V \neq \{\mathfrak{m}\}$, none of the irreducible components of ${}^a\varphi^{-1}(V)$ are contained in ${}^a\varphi^{-1}(\mathfrak{m})$. Then

$$\dim(B) = \dim(A) + \dim(k \otimes_A B).$$

Remark. By lemma 5.1 (*) clearly holds if B is A-flat, since $\{\mathfrak{m}\}$ is not the generic point of V. This justifies the remark made after proposition 5.1.

Proof: We proceed by induction on $n = \dim(A)$. $n = 0$. Then $\operatorname{Spec}(A) = \{\mathfrak{m}\}$ and $\mathfrak{m}$ is nilpotent. Hence $\mathfrak{m}B$ is contained in the nilradical of B, whence $\dim(B/\mathfrak{m}B) = \dim(B)$, and the theorem holds in this case. Assume $n > 0$, let $\mathfrak{q}_1,\ldots,\mathfrak{q}_r$ be the minimal primes of B, $\mathfrak{p}_i = \varphi^{-1}(\mathfrak{q}_i)$, $i = 1,\ldots,r$. Assume $\mathfrak{p}_i = \mathfrak{m}$ for some i, $1 \leq i \leq r$. Since $\dim(A) > 0$, there exists a prime $\mathfrak{p} \in \operatorname{Spec} A$ with $\mathfrak{p} \subsetneqq \mathfrak{m}$. Then clearly $\mathfrak{m} = \mathfrak{p}_i = \varphi^{-1}(\mathfrak{q}_i)$ implies $\mathfrak{q}_i \supset \mathfrak{p}B$. Now $V(\mathfrak{p}) \neq \{\mathfrak{m}\}$, and $\mathfrak{q}_i \supset \mathfrak{p}B \Longrightarrow \mathfrak{q}_i \in {}^a\varphi^{-1}(V(\mathfrak{p}))$, whence $\mathfrak{q}_i$ is the generic point of an irreducible component T of ${}^a\varphi^{-1}(V(\mathfrak{p}))$. From $\mathfrak{m} = \varphi^{-1}(\mathfrak{q}_i)$ we see ${}^a\varphi(\mathfrak{q}_i) = \mathfrak{m}$, whence $T \subset {}^a\varphi^{-1}(\mathfrak{m})$, contrary to assumption (*). Therefore $\mathfrak{m} \neq \mathfrak{p}_i$, $i = 1,\ldots,r$.

Let now $\mathfrak{p}'_1,\ldots,\mathfrak{p}'_s$ be the minimal primes of A. Since $\dim(A) > 0$, $\mathfrak{m} \neq \mathfrak{p}'_j$, $j = 1,\ldots,s$. Hence

$$\mathfrak{m} \not\subset \left(\bigcup_{i=1}^{r} \mathfrak{p}_i\right) \cup \left(\bigcup_{j=1}^{s} \mathfrak{p}'_j\right) = E.$$

Let $x \in \mathfrak{m}$, $x \notin E$. By proposition 2.6, since $x \notin \mathfrak{p}'_j$, $j = 1,\ldots,s$, and $\varphi(x) \notin \mathfrak{q}_i$, $i = 1,\ldots,r$

$$\dim(A/xA) = n - 1$$

$$\dim(B/xB) = \dim B - 1$$

Furthermore since $\mathrm{Spec}(A/xA) \subset \mathrm{Spec}(A)$, $\mathrm{Spec}(B/xB) \subset \mathrm{Spec}(B)$, and $\mathfrak{m}(A/xA)$ is the closed point of $\mathrm{Spec}(A/xA)$, (*) holds for A/xA and B/xB. Hence we can apply the induction assumption, whence, letting $A' = A/xA$, $B' = B/xB$, $\dim(B) - 1 = \dim(B/xB) = \dim(A/xA) + \dim(A'/_{\mathfrak{m}'} \otimes_{A'} B')$ where $\mathfrak{m}'$ denotes the unique maximal ideal $\mathfrak{m}A'$ of A'.

Now

$$A'/_{\mathfrak{m}'} = A/\mathfrak{m} \text{ and } A/\mathfrak{m} \otimes_{A/xA} B/xB =$$

$$A/\mathfrak{m} \otimes_{A/xA} (A/xA \otimes_A B) = A/\mathfrak{m} \otimes_A B$$

and finally

$$\dim(B) - 1 = \dim(A) - 1 + \dim(k \otimes_A B)$$

and the theorem is proved.

We may ask if, when equality holds in proposition 5.1, B is A-flat. The answer is yes, but under fairly strong conditions on A and B. Namely

<u>Proposition 5.2</u>. Let $\varphi: A \to B$ be a local homomorphism. Assume furthermore that

1) A is regular

2) B is C-M

3) $\dim(B) = \dim(A) + \dim(k \otimes_A B)$

Then B is A-flat.

<u>Proof</u>: We proceed by induction on $n = \dim(A)$. $n = 0$ implies A is a field (since A is regular), and any vector space over A is flat.

Let $n > 0$. Since A is regular, there exists $x \in \mathfrak{m}$, $x \notin \mathfrak{m}^2$. Since A is an integral domain x is A-regular. Let $A' = A/xA$. Then A' is also regular, by corollary 4.2, and $\dim(A') = \dim(A) - 1$ by proposition 3.1.

Let $B' = B/xB$. By proposition 5.1 we have

$$\dim(B') \leq \dim(A') + \dim(A'/\mathfrak{m}' \otimes_{A'} B')$$

where $\mathfrak{m}'$ denotes the unique maximal ideal $\mathfrak{m}A'$ of A'.

Now $A'/\mathfrak{m}' = A/\mathfrak{m} = k$, and $A/\mathfrak{m} \otimes_{A/xA} B/xB \simeq A/\mathfrak{m} \otimes_A B$. From the Hauptidealsatz we have

$$\dim(B) - 1 \leq \dim(B')$$

whence

$$\dim(B) - 1 \leq \dim(B') \leq \dim(A) - 1 + \dim(k \otimes_A B) = \dim(B) - 1.$$

Therefore $\dim(B') = \dim(B) - 1$ whence (since B is C-M), x is B-regular by proposition 3.2, whence B' is C-M.

Hence 1), 2), 3) of the statement of our proposition hold for A' and B', whence, by the induction assumption, B' is A'-flat. Now the canonical homomorphism

$$xA \otimes_A B \to xB$$

is clearly surjective and, since x is B-regular, it is also injective. Hence, by (iii) of theorem 1 of B.C.A., III, §5, no. 2, B is A-flat and the proposition is proved.

Remark. The following examples show that there is no hope of improving proposition 5.2.

Example 1. Take $A' = \mathbb{C}[T]$, $B' = \mathbb{C}[X,Y]/[(X-Y)^2(X+Y), (X-Y)(X+Y)^2]$ then let

$$f: A' \to B'$$

be defined by $f(T)$ = the class of $(X+Y)(X-Y)$, and let A,B be the localizations of A',B' at T, (X,Y) respectively. Then we have

1) B is not C-M
2) B is not A-flat

Example 2. Let $A' = \mathbb{C}[X^2, XY, Y^2]$, $B' = \mathbb{C}[X,Y]$, $f: A' \to B'$ the inclusion, A = the localization of A' at (X^2, XY, Y^2), B = the localization of B' at (X,Y). Then we have

1) A is normal and C-M
2) B is regular
3) B is not A-flat

5B. We now study the behavior of the notion of depth under local homomorphisms.

Once again, with the same notations as in section 5A, we wish to relate the depths of the three rings A, B, $B/\mathfrak{m}B$. More specifically, we shall investigate under what conditions we have

$$\operatorname{depth}(B) = \operatorname{depth}(A) + \operatorname{depth}(k \otimes_A B)$$

Unfortunately here we have no parallel to proposition 5.1, as the following two examples show:

1. Let $t \in A$ be A-regular, $B = A/tA$. Then, by theorem 3.1,

$$\operatorname{depth} B = \operatorname{depth}(A) - 1 < \operatorname{depth}(A)$$

whence we get $\operatorname{depth}(B) < \operatorname{depth}(A) + \operatorname{depth}(k \otimes_A B)$.

2. Let A be a non C-M ring with nilradical $\mathfrak{N} \neq 0$. Let $B = A/\mathfrak{N}$. If dim(A) = 1 we have dim(B) = 1, and since A is not C-M depth(A) = 0, depth($B/\mathfrak{m}B$) = 0 (since $A \to B \to 0$ is exact, $\mathfrak{m}B$ is a maximal ideal and $B/\mathfrak{m}B$ is a field). But depth(B) = 1. To see this, let $\mathfrak{p}_1, \ldots, \mathfrak{p}_t$ be the minimal primes of A. Since dim(A) = 1, $\mathfrak{m} \neq \mathfrak{p}_i$, $i = 1, \ldots, t$, whence $\mathfrak{m} \not\subset \bigcup_{i=1}^{t} \mathfrak{p}_i$. Let $x \in \mathfrak{m}$, $x \notin \bigcup_{i=1}^{t} \mathfrak{p}_i$, and let $\overline{x} = x + \mathfrak{N} \in B$. Since $\mathfrak{N} = \bigcap_{i=1}^{t} \mathfrak{p}_i$, we see that $\overline{x}$ is not a zero divisor in B.

Even though, in general, depth has an irregular behavior under local homomorphisms, it does behave nicely under flat, local homomorphisms. In fact we have

Theorem 5.2. Let $\varphi: A \to B$ be a local homomorphism and assume that B is A-flat. Then

$$\text{depth}(B) = \text{depth}(A) + \text{depth}(k \otimes_A B)$$

Proof: We proceed by induction on n = depth(A) + depth($k \otimes_A B$).

1) n = 0. Then depth(A) = depth($k \otimes_A B$) = 0. Hence $\mathfrak{m} \in \text{Ass}(A)$ and $\mathfrak{n}B/\mathfrak{m}B \in \text{Ass}(B/\mathfrak{m}B)$, by theorem 3.1. Now, by Theorem 2 of B.C.A., IV, §2, no. 6, we have

$\text{Ass}(B) = \bigcup_{\mathfrak{p} \in \text{Ass}(A)} \text{Ass}(B/\mathfrak{p}B)$. Since $\mathfrak{m} \in \text{Ass}(A)$,

$\text{Ass}(B) \supset \text{Ass}(B/\mathfrak{m}B)$, whence $\mathfrak{n}(B/\mathfrak{m}B) \in \text{Ass}(B/\mathfrak{m}B)$ implies $\mathfrak{n} \in \text{Ass}(B)$. Therefore depth(B) = 0 by theorem 3.1.

2) Assume n > 0. We proceed in two steps.

Case 1. depth(A) > 0. Then there exists $x \in \mathfrak{m}$ such that x is A-regular.

Let $A' = A/xA$, $B' = B/xB$. Then

$$(A'/\mathfrak{m}A')\otimes_{A'}B' \quad = \quad (A/\mathfrak{m})\otimes_{A'}(A'\otimes_A B) \quad = \quad (A/\mathfrak{m})\otimes_A B.$$

Since B is A-flat, the exact sequence

$$0 \to A \overset{\Psi}{\to} A \qquad \Psi \text{ is multiplication by } x$$

gives an exact sequence

$$0 \to A \otimes_A B \to A \otimes_A B$$

whence x is B-regular. Hence depth(A') = depth(A) - 1, depth(B') = depth(B) - 1. Furthermore, B' is A' - flat (see proof of Lemma 5.1 or Corollary 2 of B.C.A., I, §2).

We can hence apply the induction assumption. Since

$$\text{depth}(A') + \text{depth}((A'/\mathfrak{m}A') \otimes_{A'} B') =$$

$$\text{depth}(A) - 1 + \text{depth}(k \otimes_A B)$$

we have

$$\text{depth}(B') = \text{depth}(A') + \text{depth}(k \otimes_A B)$$

whence the theorem, in this case.

Case 2. depth($B/\mathfrak{m}B$) > 0. Then there exists a $\bar{y} \in \mathfrak{n}\, B/\mathfrak{m}B$ which is $B/\mathfrak{m}B$-regular. Let $y \in \mathfrak{n}$ be such that $\bar{y} = y + \mathfrak{m}B$. The rest of the proof is based upon the following

Theorem 5.3. Let A, B be noetherian local rings, $\mathfrak{m}$, $\mathfrak{n}$ their respective maximal ideals. Let $k = A/\mathfrak{m}$ and let $\varphi: A \to B$ be a local homomorphism. Let M, N be two finitely generated B-modules, and $u: M \to N$ a B-homomorphism, whence

$$u \otimes 1 : M \otimes_A k \to N \otimes_A k$$

is a $B \otimes_A k$-homomorphism. Assume that N is A-flat. Then the following two conditions are equivalent:

1) u is injective, and coker (u) is A-flat

2) $u \otimes 1$ is injective.

<u>Proof</u>: We write gr(M) for $gr_{\mathfrak{m}}(M)$ and similarly for N. Note that

$$M \otimes_A k = gr_0(M)$$

$$N \otimes_A k = gr_0(N)$$

$$k = gr_0(A).$$

1)$\Longrightarrow$2). From the exact sequence

$$(*) \qquad 0 \to M \xrightarrow{u} N \to \text{coker}(u) \to 0$$

and from Grothendieck's E.G.A., 0, 6.1.2 we see that M is A-flat, and that $u \otimes 1$ is injective. (Tensor (*) with k.)

2) $\Longrightarrow$ 1). We have $gr_0(u) : gr_0(M) \to gr_0(N)$ is injective. Since N is A-flat, by theorem 1, B.C.A., III, 5, 2, the canonical homomorphism $\varphi : gr(A) \otimes_{gr_0(A)} gr_0(N) \to gr(N)$ is bijective. Hence we can apply proposition 9, B.C.A., III 2, 8, and thereby obtain that gr(u) is injective, and that coker(u) satisfies (iv) of theorem 1, B.C.A., III, 5, 2. (with M = coker(u), $\mathfrak{J} = \mathfrak{m}$). Since gr(u) is injective, and since the $\mathfrak{n}$-adic topology on M is Hausdorf (B is local and M is finitely generated) from Corollary 1, B.C.A., III, 2, 8, we obtain that

u is injective. Furthermore, since M and N are finitely generated B-modules, so is coker(u), and since B is noetherian, coker(u) is "idéalement séparé" for $\mathfrak{n}$. (See Definition 1, B.C.A. III, 5.1, and example 1 thereafter.) Since φ is a local homomorphism, it follows that coker(u) is "idéalement séparé" for $\mathfrak{m}$. Hence condition (iv) of theorem 1, B.C.A., III, 5, 2, implies condition (i) of the same theorem, i.e. Coker(u) is A-flat (we use here the noetherianity of A). Q.E.D.

We return to the proof of Case 2, Theorem 5.2. We had $\operatorname{depth}(B/\mathfrak{m}B) > 0$, and we had $\bar{y} \in \mathfrak{n}B/\mathfrak{m}B$, $\bar{y}$ was $B/\mathfrak{m}B$-regular, and $y \in B$ such that $\bar{y} = y + \mathfrak{m}B$. Apply Theorem 5.3 to the B-homomorphism $u: B \to B$ defined by $u(b) = y \cdot b$. Since $\bar{y}$ is $B \otimes_A k$-regular,

$$u \otimes 1 : B \otimes_A k \to B \otimes_A k$$

is injective, whence u is injective and coker(u) is A-flat, i.e. y is B-regular and $B' = B/yB = \operatorname{coker}(u)$ is A-flat. (One can easily show that, conversely, if y is B-regular then B' is A-flat.)

By Theorem 3.1, we have

$$\operatorname{depth}(B') = \operatorname{depth}(B) - 1.$$

Now $B' \otimes_A k = (B/yB) \otimes_A k = (B \otimes_A k)/\bar{y}(B \otimes_A k)$. Therefore, again by Theorem 3.1, $\operatorname{depth}(B' \otimes_A k) = \operatorname{depth}(B \otimes_A k) - 1$.

Finally $\varphi' : A \to B'$ is again local and B' is A-flat. We can therefore apply the induction assumption (since $\operatorname{depth}(A) + \operatorname{depth}(B' \otimes_A k) = [\operatorname{depth}(A) + \operatorname{depth}(B \otimes_A k)] - 1$) and we get

$$\operatorname{depth}(B) = \operatorname{depth}(B') + 1 = \operatorname{depth}(A) + \operatorname{depth}(B' \otimes {}_A k) + 1 =$$

$$\operatorname{depth}(A) + \operatorname{depth}(B \otimes {}_A k)$$

and Theorem 5.2 is proved.

Corollary 5.1. Under the same assumptions as in Theorem 5.2, B is a C-M ring, if, and only if, A and $B/\mathfrak{m}B$ are C-M rings.

Proof: From Theorems 5.1 and 5.2 we have

$$\text{(a)}\quad \dim(B) = \dim(A) + \dim(k \otimes {}_A B)$$

$$\text{(b)}\quad \operatorname{depth}(B) = \operatorname{depth}(A) + \operatorname{depth}(k \otimes {}_A B).$$

Therefore, if A and $B/\mathfrak{m}B$ are C-M rings, so, trivially is B.

Conversely, let B be a C-M ring. We have:

$$\dim(A) \geq \operatorname{depth}(A)$$

$$\dim(k \otimes {}_A B) \geq \operatorname{depth}(k \otimes {}_A B)$$

and

$$\dim(A) + \dim(k \otimes {}_A B) = \dim(B) =$$

$$\operatorname{depth}(B) = \operatorname{depth}(A) + \operatorname{depth}(k \otimes {}_A B).$$

Therefore $\dim(A) = \operatorname{depth}(A)$ and $\dim(k \otimes {}_A B) = \operatorname{depth}(k \otimes {}_A B)$, i.e. A and $B/\mathfrak{m}B$ are C-M rings. The corollary is proved.

Theorem 5.2 and Corollary 5.1 are local in nature. We are now going to examine some of the global consequences of flatness.

As usual we let A, B be two rings, X = Spec(B), Y = Spec(A), O_X = the sheaf of local rings $B_{\mathfrak{p}}$ of X, O_Y = the sheaf of local rings $A_{\mathfrak{q}}$ of Y. If $\varphi: A \to B$ is a given homomorphism the subschemes ${}^a\varphi^{-1}(y)$ of X are called the <u>fibres of X over Y</u>.

We recall that to say that X satisfies (S_k) is to say that, for all $x \in X$

$$\operatorname{depth}(O_{x,X}) \geq \min[k, \dim(O_{x,X})]$$

(See definition 4.6). We also remark that, if A is a C-M ring then X satisfies (S_k), by (3.5).

<u>Theorem 5.4</u>. Let $\varphi: A \to B$ be a homomorphism of (not necessarily local) rings. Let $X = \operatorname{Spec}(B)$, $Y = \operatorname{Spec}(A)$, and assume ${}^a\varphi: X \to Y$ is a flat morphism(i.e. B is a flat A-module under φ). Then

1) If X satisfies (S_k) so does Y
2) If Y and every fiber of X over Y satisfy (S_k) so does X.

<u>Proof</u>: 1. Let $y \in Y$, x the generic point of an irreducible component of ${}^a\varphi^{-1}(y)$. By lemma 5.1 ${}^a\varphi(x) = y$ and theorem 5.1 applies. We have to show that $\operatorname{depth}(O_{y,Y}) \geq \min[k, \dim O_{y,Y}]$. If $O_{y,Y} = A_{\mathfrak{q}}$, $O_{x,X} = B_{\mathfrak{p}}$ we have $k(y) = A_{\mathfrak{q}}/\mathfrak{q}A_{\mathfrak{q}}$, $k(x) = B_{\mathfrak{p}}/\mathfrak{p}B_{\mathfrak{p}}$ and $\varphi^{-1}(\mathfrak{p}) = \mathfrak{q}$. Furthermore $B_{\mathfrak{p}}$ is $A_{\mathfrak{q}}$-flat. Since x is the <u>generic</u> point of an irreducible component of ${}^a\varphi^{-1}(y)$, we have $\dim(B_{\mathfrak{p}}/\mathfrak{q}B_{\mathfrak{p}}) = 0$, whence $\operatorname{depth}(B_{\mathfrak{p}}/\mathfrak{q}B_{\mathfrak{p}}) = 0$. Therefore

$$0 = \dim(O_x \otimes_{O_y} k(y)) = \operatorname{depth}(O_x \otimes_{O_y} k(y))$$

By theorems 5.1 and 5.2 we obtain

$$\dim(O_x) = \dim(O_y)$$

$$\operatorname{depth}(O_x) = \operatorname{depth}(O_y)$$

and since O_x satisfies the condition (S_k), so does O_y, Q.E.D.

2) Let $x \in X$, $y = {}^a\varphi(x)$. From theorems 5.1, 5.2 we have

$$\dim(O_x) = \dim(O_y) + \dim(O_x \otimes_{O_y} k(y))$$

$$\operatorname{depth}(O_x) = \operatorname{depth}(O_y) + \operatorname{depth}(O_x \otimes_{O_y} k(y))$$

By assumption both O_y and $O_x \otimes_{O_y} k(y)$ satisfy the condition of (S_k). Hence so does O_x, Q.E.D.

(Note that here we do not know that x is the generic point of an irreducible component of ${}^a\varphi^{-1}(y)$!).

The answer to the following question is at the moment unkown: Let A, B be local rings $\varphi: A \to B$ a local flat morphism. If A and $B/\mathfrak{m}B$ satisfy (S_k), does B satisfy (S_k)? The crucial difference between the situation here and the one in theorem 5.4 is that here we assume (S_k) only for the fiber of Spec(B) over the closed point of Spec(A), while in 2) of theorem 5.4 (S_k) is assumed for all fibers.

The previous theorem dealt with the behavior of the condition (S_k) under global flat morphism. We now examine the behavior of the notion of regularity in the local case.

Theorem 5.5. Let A, B be noetherian, local rings, $\varphi: A \to B$ a local morphism and let B be a A-flat. Then

1) If B is regular, so is A
2) If A and $B/\mathfrak{m}B$ are regular, so is B.

Proof: 1) Since B is A-flat, the same argument as in the proof of Corollary 4.3 (replacing $A_{\mathfrak{p}}$ with B) shows that

$$\text{coh. dim}(B) \leq \text{coh. dim}(A).$$

1) is therefore a trivial consequence of the Hilbert-Serre theorem (theorem 4.2).

2) Let dim(A) = m, and let $x_1, \ldots, x_m$ be a regular system of parameters of A. Since B is A-flat, $\varphi(x_1), \ldots, \varphi(x_m)$ are B-regular. (Tensor the exact sequence $0 \to A/x_1A + \ldots + x_{i-1}A \to A/x_1A + \ldots + x_{i-1}A$ with B.) Now by assumption $B/\mathfrak{m}B = B/\varphi(x_1)\,B + \ldots + \varphi(x_m)\,B$ is regular. Therefore by proposition 4.1, B is regular. (Replace A with B and $\mathfrak{J}$ with $\mathfrak{m}B$ in the proposition.)

Corollary 5.2. Let A be a ring, $T_1, \ldots, T_n$ independent transcendentals over A. Then:

i) If A is regular, so is $A[T_1, \ldots, T_n]$ (in particular if k is a field, $k[T_1, \ldots, T_n]$ is regular).

ii) If A is C-M, so is $A[T_1, \ldots, T_n]$ (in particular, if k is a field, $k[T_1, \ldots, T_n]$ is C-M).

Proof: Clearly it suffices to prove i) and ii) when n = 1, the general case following by induction. Let now B = A[T]. Since B is A-free, it is A-flat. Let $\mathfrak{m}$ be a maximal ideal of B, $\mathfrak{n}$ the prime ideal of A given by $\mathfrak{n} = \mathfrak{m} \cap A$. Then $B_{\mathfrak{m}}$ is $A_{\mathfrak{n}}$-flat and, by theorem 5.5, to prove i) and ii) it suffices to show that $A_{\mathfrak{n}}$ and $B_{\mathfrak{m}}/\mathfrak{n}B_{\mathfrak{m}}$ are regular, and C-M, respectively, under the corresponding assumptions for A. That $A_{\mathfrak{n}}$ is regular when A is regular follows from Corollary 4.3 to Hilbert-Serre theorem (theorem 4.2). If A is C-M, then so is $A_{\mathfrak{n}}$ by proposition 3.5.

Now

$$B_{\mathfrak{m}}/\mathfrak{n}B_{\mathfrak{m}} = (B/\mathfrak{n}B)_{\mathfrak{m}(B/\mathfrak{n}B)} =$$

$$((A/\mathfrak{n}) \otimes {}_A B)_{\mathfrak{m}(B/\mathfrak{n}B)} = k[T]_{\mathfrak{m}'}$$

where $k = A_{\mathfrak{n}}/\mathfrak{n}A_{\mathfrak{n}}$ and $\mathfrak{m}'$ is the canonical image of $\mathfrak{m}(B/\mathfrak{n}B)$ in k[T]. k[T] is a principal ideal domain, $k[T]_{\mathfrak{m}'}$ is a discrete valuation ring, hence regular and, a fortiori, C-M (Corollary 4.1). The theorem is proved.

Having examined the behavior of dimension, depth, (S_k), and regularity under flat morphisms, we complete the analysis with the study of the behavior of condition (R_k).

Let as usual $\varphi: A \to B$ be a flat morphism, and let $X = \mathrm{Spec}(B)$, $Y = \mathrm{Spec}(A)$, $f = {}^a\varphi: X \to Y$. We say that X satisfies (R_k) if the ring B does, and similarly for the spectrum of any ring. We remark that to say X satisfies (R_k) is equivalent to saying that, when $\dim O_x \leq k$, O_x is regular. (see definition 4.6) Now:

<u>Theorem 5.6</u>. Let $\varphi: A \to B$ be a flat morphism. Then:

1) If X satisfies (R_k) so does Y

2) If Y and $f^{-1}(y)$ satisfy (R_k), for all $y \in Y$, so does X.

<u>Proof</u>: Let $y \in Y$, $x \in f^{-1}(y)$. Since B is A-flat we have that O_x is O_y-flat, whence, by Theorem 5.1

$$(*) \qquad \dim(O_x) = \dim(O_y) + \dim(O_x \otimes_{O_y} k(y))$$

where $k(y) = O_y/\mathfrak{m}_y$.

1) We have to prove that O_y is regular if $\dim(O_y) \leq k$. If we choose x to be the generic point of an irreducible component of $f^{-1}(y)$, we have $\dim(O_x \otimes_{O_y} k(y)) = 0$ (since $B_{j_x}/j_y B_{j_x}$ is artinian), whence

$$\dim O_x = \dim O_y \leq k$$

and therefore O_x is regular. Then, by theorem 5.5, O_y is regular and 1) is proved.

2) Let now $x \in X$ be arbitrary, $\dim O_x \leq k$, and let $y = f(x)$. We have to show that O_x is regular. From equation (*) above we have $\dim(O_y) \leq k$ and $\dim(O_x \otimes_{O_y} k(y)) \leq k$. By assumption (R_k) holds for Y and $f^{-1}(y) = \mathrm{Spec}(B \otimes_A k(y))$. Hence O_y and $O_x \otimes_{O_y} k(y)$ are regular (note that $O_x \otimes_{O_y} k(y)$ is the local ring of x in $f^{-1}(y)$!), and by theorem 5.5, O_x is regular,

Q.E.D.

A quick comparison shows that theorems 5.4 and 5.6 are identical if one replaces (S_k) by (R_k). It is then natural to ask the same question about (R_k) that was asked about (S_k) after the end of the proof of the theorem namely: Let A, B be local rings, $\varphi: A \to B$ a local flat morphism. If A and $B/\mathfrak{m}B$ satisfy (R_k), does B satisfy (R_k)?

As with (S_k), the crucial difference between the situation here and the one in theorem 5.6 is that here we assume (R_k) only for the fiber of Spec(B) over the closed point of Spec(A), while in theorem 5.6 we assume (R_k) for all fibers. Here the answer is known, in the negative. As usual the counter example is due to Nagata.

The following theorem is an immediate application of theorems 5.4 and 5.6, coupled with the characterization of reduced (normal) rings given in propositions 4.5 and 4.6.

Theorem 5.7. Let $\varphi : A \to B$ be a flat homomorphism of (not necessarily local) noetherian rings. Then:

1) If B is reduced (normal), so is A
2) If, for every $\mathfrak{p} \in \mathrm{Spec}(A)$, A and B/ B are reduced (normal), so is B.

Proof: Obvious.

We complete this section with a few remarks concerning the following situation.

A field k, a noetherian overring A of k, and a field $k' \supset k$ are given. The ring $A' = A \otimes_k k'$ is an overring of k'. We leave to the reader the verification of the following statements:

Proposition 5.3.

1) A' is noetherian if $[k':k] < \infty$ (A' need not be noetherian in general).
2) If A is a local ring, A' is semi-local.
3) A' is a flat A-module.
4) If $x' \in \mathrm{Spec}(A')$, x = the image of x', then $\dim A_x = \dim A'_{x'}$.
5) Under the same assumption as in 4), $\mathrm{depth}(A_x) = \mathrm{depth}(A'_{x'})$.
6) Under the same assumption as in 4), A_x is C-M if, and only if, $A'_{x'}$ is C-M.

7) A satisfies (S_k) if, and only if A' satisfies (S_k).

1, 2) and 3) have easy proofs. To prove 4), 5), 6), 7) apply theorems 5.1, 5.2, corollary 5.1, and theorem 5.4.

Theorem 5.8. Let k be a field, A an overring of k, k' a field containing k, $A' = A \otimes_k k'$. If A' is, respectively, regular, (R_k), normal, reduced, then A is regular (R_k), normal, reduced.

Proof: Follows directly from the previous results of this section.

In general, however, A' need not be regular if A is, as the following example shows:

Let k be a non perfect field $k \neq k^p$, $p > 2$ and let $a \in k$, $a \notin k^p$. Let

$$A = k[X, Y]/(Y^2 - X^p + a)$$

The Jacobian criterion (Proposition 4.3) tells us that A is regular. Now let $k' = k(a^{1/p})$. Then one easily verifies, from $X^p - a = (X - a^{1/p})^p$ that

$$A' \simeq k'[X, Y]/(Y^2 - X^p)$$

and again proposition 4.3 tells us that A' is not regular.

We leave as an exercise to the reader the proof of the following

Theorem 5.9. Under the same assumption as in theorem 5.8, if A is regular and k' is a separable extension of k, then A' is regular.

Theorem 5.9 prompts us to introduce the following

Definition 5.1. Let k be a field, A an overring of k. The ring A is said to be geometrically regular if, for all finite field extensions k' of k, the ring $A' = A \otimes_k k'$ is regular.

Corollary 5.3. a) Every regular overring of a perfect field is geometrically regular. .

b) Every regular overring of an algebraically closed field is geometrically regular.

Remark. Let again $A' = A \otimes_k k'$. Some of the properties of A' can be deduced from those of A and of the field extension k' of k. This process of deduction is known as ascent. Conversely, some of the properties of A can be deduced from those of A'. This latter process of deduction is known as descent.

§6. COMPLETION AND NORMALIZATION

6A. Completion. Let A be a noetherian local ring, $\mathfrak{m}$ its maximal ideal. It is well known(see Corollary after Proposition 5 in B.C.A., III, §3, no. 2) that $\bigcap \mathfrak{m}^n = (0)$. This implies that the collection $\{\mathfrak{m}^n\}$ can be taken as the basis of a filter of neighborhoods of 0 in a (unique) Hausdorff topology which is consistent with the ring structure of A (i.e. A is a Hausdorff topological ring).

The set $\hat{A}$ of (equivalence classes of) Cauchy sequences of elements of A can be given a topological ring structure which is obviously complete (i.e. every Cauchy sequence in $\hat{A}$ is convergent). We refer the reader to the third chapter of B.C.A. for the proof of the above statements, as well as for the proof of the following ones, for which we give references to be found in the above mentioned third chapter.

1) The canonical homomorphism

$$j: A \to \widehat{A}$$

is a monomorphism (§2, no. 12, since A is Hausdorff).

2) $\widehat{A}$ is a noetherian local ring, with unique maximal ideal $\widehat{\mathfrak{m}} = \mathfrak{m}\widehat{A}$. (§3, no. 4, Corollary to Proposition 8, and §2, no. 12, Corollary 2)

3) $\widehat{A}$ is a faithfully flat A-module (§3, no. 5, proposition 9)

4) $\widehat{A} = \varprojlim (A/\mathfrak{m}^n)$ (§3, no. 6)

5) $A/\mathfrak{m} \simeq \widehat{A}/\widehat{\mathfrak{m}} = \widehat{A}/\mathfrak{m}\widehat{A}$. (Apply equation (21) in §3, no. 12, and 2) above.)

Example. Let P(X, Y) be the polynomial $Y^2 - X^2(X + 1)$ whose variety of zeros in the affine plane is the cubic with double point represented in the figure. Let $B = \mathbb{C}[X,Y]/(P)$ and let $\mathfrak{m}$ be the maximal ideal of B generated by (the equivalence classes of) X and Y. Let $A = B_{\mathfrak{m}}$. One easily sees that

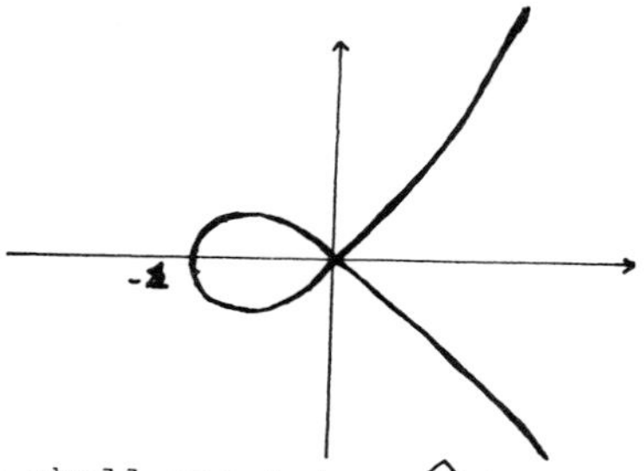

A is an integral domain, but, as we shall see later, $\widehat{A}$ is not integral, it has in fact two distinct minimal prime ideals. (See Theorem 6.5.)

We now consider the ascent and descent properties of the local morphism $A \to \widehat{A}$.

Proposition 6.1. A noetherian local ring A is,

respectively, regular or C-M if, and only if, its completion $\hat{A}$ is regular or C-M. If $\hat{A}$ is, respectively, reduced or normal, then so is A.

<u>Proof</u>: The morphism $A \to \hat{A}$ is flat. Hence we can apply the results of §5. Since $\hat{A}/\mathfrak{m}\hat{A} = A/\mathfrak{m}$, the first assertion of our proposition is a consequence of theorem 5.5 and corollary 5.1 respectively. The second assertion follows from theorem 5.7.

The converse of the second statement in proposition 5.1 is false, as shown by a counter example due to Nagata. If, however, the fibers of the morphism $\mathrm{Spec}(\hat{A}) \to \mathrm{Spec}(A)$ (called <u>formal fibers</u>) are regular or geometrically regular, then a simple application of theorems 5.4 and 5.6, and propositions 4.5 and 4.6 shows that, when A is either reduced or normal, then so is $\hat{A}$.

Having introduced complete local rings, we turn our attention to the study of some of their properties.

<u>Definition 6.1</u>. Let A, B be noetherian local rings, with maximal ideals $\mathfrak{m}, \mathfrak{n}$ respectively. Let $\varphi: A \to B$ be a local homomorphism. B is called a <u>Cohen algebra over A</u> if the following three properties hold:

i) B is complete

ii) B is A-flat

iii) $B/\mathfrak{m}B$ is a separable field extension of $A/\mathfrak{m}$.

A trivial example of Cohen algebra is a separable field extension of a field.

We state without proof two theorems, which will be used in the proof of the main result of this section. (For the proofs see E.G.A., Chap. 0_{IV}, 19.3.10 and 19.7.2.)

Theorem 6.1. Let B be a Cohen algebra, over a noetherian local ring A, and let C be a complete noetherian local ring which is an A-algebra under a local homomorphism $\varphi : A \to C$. Let J be a closed ideal in C. Then for any A-homomorphism $\Psi : B \to C/J$ there exists a local A-homomorphism $\theta : B \to C$ such that the following diagram commutes

$$\begin{array}{ccc} B & \xrightarrow{\theta} & C \\ & \Psi\searrow & \swarrow \\ & C/J & \end{array}$$

Theorem 6.2. Let A be a noetherian local ring, $\mathfrak{m}$ its maximal ideal, $k = A/\mathfrak{m}$, K a separable extension of k. Then there exists a unique (up to A-isomorphisms) Cohen algebra B over A, such that $B/\mathfrak{m}B \simeq K$.

We denote by Z_p the localization of the ring Z at the principal prime ideal pZ. The rings $\widehat{Z_p}$ are called the _complete prime local rings_. One trivially sees that every local ring is a Z_p-algebra for an appropriate prime $p \geq 0$, and contains it, and that every complete local ring is a $\widehat{Z_p}$-algebra, again for an appropriate prime p.

With this in mind we give the following

Definition 6.2. A ring B is called a _Cohen ring_ if it is a Cohen algebra over a complete prime local ring.

As an easy application of theorem 6.2 we obtain

Proposition 6.2. For each separable extension L of the field $\Pi_p = Z_p/pZ_p$ ($\Pi_0 = Q$) there exists a unique (up to isomorphisms) Cohen ring B, over $\widehat{Z_p}$, having L as residual field.

This clearly describes _all_ Cohen rings.

We can now state and prove the main theorem of this section, namely:

Theorem 6.3. (Cohen Structure Theorem for Complete Local Rings). Let A be a complete, noetherian local ring. Then:

1) There exists either a Cohen ring W or a field k such that $A \simeq W[[T_1,\dots,T_n]]/\mathfrak{a}$, for an appropriate ideal $\mathfrak{a} \subset W[[T_1,\dots,T_n]]$. If A contains a field k one can take W = k.

2) If in addition A is an integral domain, then there exists a subring $B \subset A$ such that the following properties hold:

a) B is isomorphic either to $k[[T_1,\dots,T_n]]$, where $k = A/\mathfrak{m}$, or to $W[[T_1,\dots,T_n]]$, where W is a Cohen ring.

b) A and B have the same residue field.

c) A is a finitely generated B-module.

3) If in addition A is regular, then A is isomorphic either to $k[[T_1,\dots,T_n]]$, $k = A/\mathfrak{m}$, or to $W[[T_1,\dots,T_n]]$, W a Cohen ring.

Remark. The above theorem classifies all complete noetherian regular local rings, as we asserted in the section on regular local rings.

Proof: If A contains a field, say k", let P denote its prime field. We have the diagram $P \to A \to k = A/\mathfrak{m}$ whence k is a Cohen algebra over P, since P is perfect. Therefore, by theorem 6.1, we obtain the commutative diagram

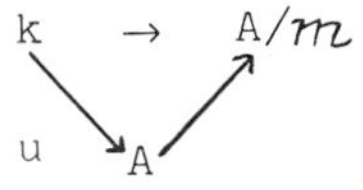

and u is necessarily injective, i.e. A contains a copy k' of k.

If A contains no field, then A is a $\hat{Z}_p$-algebra, for some appropriate prime $p > 0$, (otherwise A contains $Z_{(0)} = Q$), and $\mathrm{char}(k) = p$. By theorem 6.2 there exists a Cohen ring W over $\hat{Z}_p$ such that its residue field is isomorphic to k. Since A is a $\hat{Z}_p$-algebra and $\mathfrak{m}$ is closed in A we can apply theorem 6.1 in this case also, and obtain the commutative diagram

$$\begin{array}{ccc} W & \rightarrow & A/\mathfrak{m} \\ & {}_{u}\searrow \quad \nearrow & \\ & A & \end{array}$$

where u is a local homomorphism.

Let now $x_1, \ldots, x_n$ be a set of elements of $\mathfrak{m}$. Define a map $v: W[[T_1, \ldots, T_n]] \rightarrow A$ $(v: k[[T_1, \ldots, T_n]] \rightarrow A)$ according to the following rules

1) $v|W = u$ $\qquad\qquad (v|k = u)$

2) $v(T_i) = x_i, \quad i = 1, \ldots, n$

The completeness of A and the fact that the x_i's are trivially topologically nilpotent, guarantee the existence and uniqueness of the homomorphism v. (See B.C.A., III, §4, no. 5)

Having disposed of the above preliminaries, we proceed with the proof of the three statements of the theorem.

1) Take $\{x_i\}$ $i = 1, \ldots, n$ to be a set of generators of $\mathfrak{m}$. Let $\mathfrak{n}$ be the maximal ideal of $W[[T_1, \ldots T_n]]$ (of $k[[T_1, \ldots, T_n]]$). Consider the homomorphism

$$gr(v): gr_{\mathfrak{n}}(W[[T_1, \ldots, T_n]]) \rightarrow gr_{\mathfrak{m}}(A)$$

$$(gr(v): gr_{\mathfrak{n}}(k[[T_1, \ldots, T_n]]) \rightarrow gr_{\mathfrak{m}}(A))$$

Since $W \to A/\mathfrak{m}$ $(k \to A/\mathfrak{m})$ is surjective, the choice of $x_1, \ldots, x_n$ shows that $gr(u)$ is surjective. Then by Corollary 2 of B.C.A., III, §2, no. 8, we have that v is surjective, and 1) is proved.

2) We consider two cases:

<u>Case 1</u>. A contains a copy k' of $k = A/\mathfrak{m}$ (see preliminary remarks). Let dim A = n and let $y_1, \ldots, y_n \in \mathfrak{m}$ be a system of parameters of A. Define $B = k[[T_1, \ldots, T_n]]$ and consider the homomorphism $v: B \to A$ as constructed in the proof of 1).

<u>Case 2</u>. A does not contain a field. Since A is an integral, local domain, for an appropriate prime integer $p > 0$, A contains a copy of Z_p. (See remark preceding definition 6.2) Identify Z_p with its image in A and note that $p \in \mathfrak{m}$ and that p is not a zero divisor of A, hence by proposition 3.3, p can be imbedded in a system $\{p, y_1, \ldots, y_{n-1}\}$ of parameters of A. From the commutative diagram (see preliminary remarks to proof)

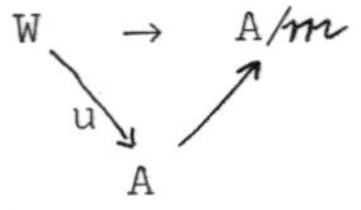

and the fact that $u(1_W) = 1_A$ we see that $p' \neq 0$ where p' denotes the element $p \cdot 1$ of W. Since u is local, $p' \in \mathfrak{n}'$, the maximal ideal of W. Let $B = W[[T_1, \ldots, T_n]]$, and define the homomorphism $v: B \to A$ as in the proof of 1). Note that $v(T_i) = y_i$, $i = 1, \ldots, n-1$, and $v(p') = p$.

In either case 1) or case 2) we have obtained a homomorphism $v: B \to A$, where $B = W[[T_1, \ldots, T_r]]$, $r = n, n-1$, W a field or a Cohen algebra over A respectively. We assert:

i) B and A have isomorphic residue field k

ii) A is a finitely generated B-module

iii) v is injective.

Clearly the above three assertions imply 2) of the theorem. We proceed to prove them.

i) We leave as an exercise to the reader the proof that, for any local ring C, the two local rings C, $C[[T_1,\dots,T_n]]$ have isomorphic residue fields.

ii) By the construction of v we clearly have, letting $\mathfrak{n}$ be the maximal ideal of B,

$$\mathfrak{n} A \subset \mathfrak{m} \subset A$$

Furthermore, since $\mathfrak{n}A$ is generated by a system of parameters of A, $\mathfrak{n}A$ is an ideal of definition of A (Definition 2.5 and Proposition 2.1), and therefore $\mathfrak{m} \supset \mathfrak{n} A \supset \mathfrak{m}^h$ for some integer $h > 0$. We have $A/\mathfrak{n} A = (A/\mathfrak{m}^h)/(\mathfrak{n} A/\mathfrak{m}^h)$.

Now, $A/\mathfrak{m}$ is (trivially) a finitely generated B-module, and since $\mathfrak{m}^q/\mathfrak{m}^{q+1}$ is a finitely generated $A/\mathfrak{m}$-module, $\mathfrak{m}^q/\mathfrak{m}^{q+1}$ is a finitely generated B-module for all $q > 0$. From the exact sequences

$$0 \to \mathfrak{m}/\mathfrak{m}^2 \to A/\mathfrak{m}^2 \to A/\mathfrak{m} \to 0$$

$$0 \to \mathfrak{m}^2/\mathfrak{m}^3 \to A/\mathfrak{m}^3 \to A/\mathfrak{m}^2 \to 0$$

$$0 \to \mathfrak{m}^{h-1}/\mathfrak{m}^h \to A/\mathfrak{m}^h \to A/\mathfrak{m}^{h-1} \to 0$$

we obtain (proceeding by induction), that $A/\mathfrak{m}^h$ is a finitely generated B-module, and therefore $A/\mathfrak{n} A$, as a quotient module of $A/\mathfrak{m}^h$, is also a finitely generated B-module.

Let $\{\bar{a}_j\}_{j=1,\ldots t}$ be a set of generators of $A/\mathfrak{n}A$ over B, and let $a_j \in A$ such that $\bar{a}_j = a_j + \mathfrak{n}A$, $j = 1,\ldots,t$. Let F be the submodule of A generated over B by $a_1,\ldots,a_t$. Then $\mathfrak{n}A + F = A$. Since B is complete we can apply (ii) of Corollary 3 of B.C.A.'s, III, §2, no. 9, and obtain that A is a finitely generated B-module, and assertion ii) is proved.

To prove (iii) we observe first of all that, since A is an integral domain, ker(v) is a prime ideal of B. Furthermore, since W is an integral domain, B is an integral domain. Finally, both in case 1 and case 2 we have dim(B) = dim(A). This is seen by observing that, in case 1, $T_1,\ldots,T_n$ is a system of parameters of B, while in case 2, p', $T_1,\ldots,T_{n-1}$ is a system of parameters of B. Therefore ker(v) = 0, otherwise dim(B) > dim(A). Assertion 2) of the theorem is proved.

3) Let $y_1,\ldots,y_n$ be a regular system of parameters of A, with $y_1 = p$ if A contains no field. (See case 2 in the proof of 2)). We obtain a homomorphism

$$v:W[[T_1,\ldots,T_r]] \to A$$

where r = n or n - 1 and W is either the field k or a Cohen ring over $\widehat{Z}_p$, according as A does or does not contain a field. By the proof of 1) v is surjective, and by the proof of 2) v is injective, whence 3) follows. The theorem is proved.

<——————————>

6B. Normalization. In this part of the present section all rings shall be assumed to be integral domains unless otherwise specified. If A is one such ring and L is a field containing A (and containing a fortiori the field of fractions K of A), we denote by A'_L the integral closure of A in L, i.e. the subring of L consisting of all those elements of L satisfying an equation of integral dependence over A. A'_L is called the <u>normalization</u> of A in L.

In particular A is called <u>normal</u> (<u>integrally closed</u>) if $A'_K = A$. From now on we shall write A' for A'_K.

Examples of normal and not-normal rings abound in Algebraic Geometry. The following two rings are easily seen to be not normal (in both cases the element T is integral over the given ring, but outside it):

Let $R_1 = \mathbb{C}[T^2, T^3]$, $R_2 = \mathbb{C}[T^2-1, T(T^2-1)]$, $\mathfrak{m}_1 = T^2 R_1$, $\mathfrak{m}_2 = (T^2-1)R_2$. Then $A_1 = (R_1)_{\mathfrak{m}_1}$; $A_2 = (R_2)_{\mathfrak{m}_2}$.

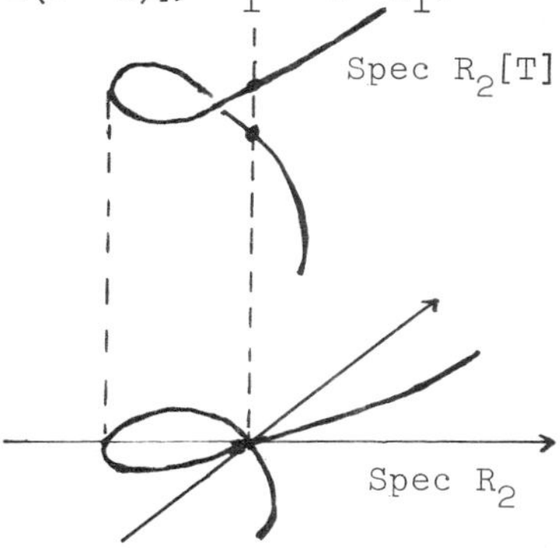

In both cases we have $K = \mathbb{C}(T)$, and

$$A'_1 = A_1[T]$$

$$A'_2 = A_2[T]$$

In the case of A'_2 we see that it has two maximal ideals, namely $(T-1)A'_2$ and $(T+1)A'_2$ (see figure). In this case the number of maximal ideals in A'_2 equals the number of minimal primeideals in the completion $\hat{A}_2$ of A_2. (See example on page 101). This is in fact a situation that repeats itself in many cases as we shall later see.

With reference to the above two examples, if L is a finite extension of K one easily sees that in these cases A'_{i_L} is a finitely generated A_i-module. In fact it is well known (E.

Noether) that if A is noetherian and char(K) = 0, then for any finite extension L of K the ring A'_L is a finitely generated A-module.

If char(K) $\neq$ 0 however, the situation is completely different. Nagata has given examples where, respectively, A is a discrete valuation ring, a noetherian local ring of dimension 2, a noetherian local ring of dimension 3, $[L:K] < \infty$ and, respectively A'_L is not a finite A-module, A'_L is not noetherian, A' is not noetherian.

We are therefore led to the following

Definition 6.3. An integral domain A, with field of fractions K, is said to be Japanese if, for every finite extension L of K, $[L:K] < \infty$, A'_L is a finitely generated A-module. A is said to be universally Japanese if every finitely generated algebra over A (in particular A itself) is Japanese.

Proposition 6.3. Let A be a noetherian integral domain, K its field of fractions. If, for every finite, purely inseparable field extension K' of K, $A'_{K'}$ is a finitely generated A-module, then A is Japanese.

Proof: The proof is based on the following two statements:

a) For every finite, field extension L of K there exists a finite field extension $\bar{L}$ of L such that every polynomial $f(X) \in K[X]$ with a root in $\bar{L}$ factors completely in $\bar{L}$.

b) If L is the field constructed in a) above there exists a field K', $K \subset K' \subset \bar{L}$ such that K' is purely inseparable over K and L is separable algebraic over K'.

See Theorem 14 of Zariski-Samuel "Commutative Algebra",

Volume I, Chapter II. Now, by assumption $A'_{K'}$ is a finitely generated A-module, and by proposition 18 of B.C.A., V, §1, no. 6, the integral closure of $A'_{K'}$ in $\bar{L}$ is a finitely generated $A'_{K'}$-module.

Clearly such integral closure is $A'_{\bar{L}}$, and we have therefore proved that $A'_{\bar{L}}$ is a finitely generated A-module. Since $A'_L \subset A'_{\bar{L}}$, and A is noetherian, A'_L is a finitely generated A-module, and the proposition is proved.

When char(K) = 0 every normal ring is (trivially!) Japanese.

The following theorem, the main one in this section, gives us a large class of Japanese rings.

Theorem 6.4. (Nagata) Every noetherian complete, local, integral domain is Japanese.

The proof uses two lemmas, the second due to Tate, which we proceed to state and prove.

Lemma 6.1. Let A be a ring and x an element of A which is not a zero divisor. If $\mathfrak{p} = x \cdot A$ is a prime ideal of A, then the inverse image of the ideal $x^n A_{\mathfrak{p}}$ under the canonical homomorphism $\varphi : A \to A_{\mathfrak{p}}$ is the ideal $x^n A$.

Proof: Clearly $\varphi(x^n A) \subset x^n A_{\mathfrak{p}}$, whence $x^n A \subset \varphi^{-1}(x^n A_{\mathfrak{p}})$. To prove $x^n A \supset \varphi^{-1}(x^n A_{\mathfrak{p}})$ we proceed by induction. If n = 1 and $y \in A$ is such that $\frac{y}{1} = \frac{xa}{f}$, $f \notin \mathfrak{p}$, then, for some $g \notin \mathfrak{p}$ $gfy = gxa$. Since $\mathfrak{p}$ is prime $gf \notin \mathfrak{p}$, whence $y \in \mathfrak{p} = xA$ and we are done in this case. For the general case, let $b \in A$ such that $b/1 = x^n a/s$, $s \notin \mathfrak{p}$. Then for some $s' \notin \mathfrak{p}$, $s'sb = s'x^n a$, whence $b \in \mathfrak{p}$ and therefore $b = x b'$. Therefore $x(s'sb' - s'x^{n-1} a) = 0$ and since x is not a zero divisor in A,

$s'sb' - s'x^{n-1} a = 0$, whence $b'/1 \in x^{n-1} A_{\mathfrak{p}}$. By induction we have $b' \in x^{n-1} A$ and the lemma is proved.

Lemma 6.2. (Tate) Let A be a noetherian integral domain, $x \neq 0$ an element of A. Assume that the following conditions hold:

i) A is integrally closed

ii) The ideal $\mathfrak{p} = x \cdot A$ is a prime ideal of A and A is complete and Hausdorff for the $\mathfrak{p}$-adic topology

iii) A/xA is Japanese.

Then A is Japanese.

Proof: Let K be the field of fractions of A, K' a finite extension of K. By Proposition 6.3 it suffices to show that $A'_{K'}$ is a finitely generated A-module when K' is a purely inseparable extension of K, say $(K')^q \subset K$, $q = p^e$, $0 < p = \text{char}(K)$. (As we remarked after Proposition 6.3, if $\text{char}(K) = 0$ A is trivially a Japanese ring.) Let K(y) be a purely inseparable extension of K such that $y^q = x$. Then, if $K'' = K' \cdot K(y)$, we have $(K'')^q \subset K$. Furthermore, if $A'_{K''}$ is a finitely generated A-module, so is $A'_{K'}$. Hence we can assume that there exists $y \in K'$ such that $y^q = x$. Denote $A'_{K'}$ by A'. Since A is integrally closed we have $A' \cap K = A$, whence

$$A' = \{x' \in K' \mid x'^q \in A\}$$

Let now $V = A_{\mathfrak{p}}$; $\mathfrak{m} = \mathfrak{p} A_{\mathfrak{p}} = xA_{\mathfrak{p}}$. Since the maximal ideal of V is generated by one regular element (A is an integral domain) V is a discrete valuation ring. In fact, by part d) of theorem 4.1, V is a regular, one dimensional local ring, hence by proposition 9 of B.C.A., Chapter VI, §3, V is a discrete valuation ring. Let V' be the integral closure of V in K'. Since V is integrally closed (Corollary 4.1), $V' \cap K = V$, and therefore

$$V' = \{x' \in K' \mid x'^q \in V\}.$$

$$\begin{array}{ccc} K & — & K' \\ | & & | \\ V & — & V' \\ | & & | \\ A & — & A' \end{array}$$

By Corollary 2 of B.C.A., Chapter VI, §8, no 6, V' is a valuation ring, and by Corollary 3, Chapter VI, §8, no 1, V' is a discrete valuation ring. Letting $\mathfrak{m}'$ denote the maximal ideal of V', by Proposition 5, Chapter VI, §8, no 5, $V'/\mathfrak{m}'$ is an extension of finite degree of $V/\mathfrak{m}$, and

$$\mathfrak{m}' = \{x' \in K' \mid x'^q \in \mathfrak{m}\}.$$

We prove the following three statements:

a) $\mathfrak{m}'^{\,n} \cap A' = y^n A'$

b) The x A'-adic topology on A' is Hausdorff

c) A'/xA' is a finitely generated A-module.

To prove a) we observe first that, since $y^q = x \in \mathfrak{m}$, $y \in \mathfrak{m}'$, and that clearly $y \in A'$. Hence $y^n A' \subset \mathfrak{m}'^n \cap A'$. Conversely, let $x' \in \mathfrak{m}'^n \cap A'$, and let $x' = y^n z'$, $z' \in K'$. We need to show $z' \in A'$. Now, since $x' \in \mathfrak{m}'^n$, we can write

$$x' = \Sigma\, t'_1 \ldots . t'_n \qquad t'_j \in \mathfrak{m}'$$

whence $(x')^q = \Sigma(t'_1)^q \ldots . (t'_n)^q$ and by the above characterization of $\mathfrak{m}'$, $(t'_j)^q \in \mathfrak{m}$, whence $(x')^q \in \mathfrak{m}^n$. Furthermore, by the characterization of A', $(x')^q \in A$, whence $(x')^q \in \mathfrak{m}^n \cap A$.

By lemma 6.1 $\mathfrak{m}^n \cap A = x^n A$, and we therefore obtain

$$y^{nq}(z')^q = (x')^q \in x^n A$$

whence $x^n(z')^q \in x^n A$, and, from the fact that A is an integral domain, $(z')^q \in A$. Therefore $z' \in A'$ and statement a) is proved.

We now prove b). Since $xA' = y^q A'$, the xA'-adic topology on A' and the yA'-adic topology on A' clearly coincide. Furthermore, by a) the yA'-adic topology on A' is induced by the $\mathfrak{m}'$-adic topology on V', which is Hausdorff since V' is a local ring. Therefore the xA'-adic topology of A' is Hausdorff.

Next, we prove c). We have $y^q = x$, and therefore $A'/xA' = A'/y^q A'$. The exact sequences

$$0 \to y^k A'/y^{k+1}A' \to A'/y^{k+1}A' \to A'/y^k A' \to 0 \qquad 0 < k \leq q-1$$

show that it suffices to show that A'/yA' and $y^k A'/y^{k+1}A'$, $k = 1,\ldots,q-1$ are finitely generated A-modules. The diagram

$$\begin{array}{ccccccccc} 0 \to & yA' & \to & A' & \to & A'/yA' & \to 0 & & \\ & \varphi\downarrow & & \varphi\downarrow & & \downarrow\overline{\varphi} & & & \\ 0 \to & y^{k+1}A' & \to & y^k A' & \to & y^k A'/y^{k+1}A' & \to 0 & & k = 1,\ldots,q-1 \end{array}$$

where $\varphi(\xi) = y^k \xi$ and $\overline{\varphi}$ is the induced homomorphism, shows that $\overline{\varphi}$ is an isomorphism, since φ is. Hence it suffices to show that A'/yA' is a finitely generated A-module. Now, by a) $yA' = \mathfrak{m}' \cap A'$, whence $A'/yA' \simeq A'/\mathfrak{m}' \cap A'$ and $A'/\mathfrak{m}' \cap A'$ is a submodule of $V'/\mathfrak{m}'$. Also, since A' is integral over A, $A'/\mathfrak{m}' \cap A'$ is integral over $A/\mathfrak{p}$. Since $V'/\mathfrak{m}'$ is a finite extension of $V/\mathfrak{m}$, and $A/\mathfrak{p}$ is Japanese by assumption, the integral closure of $A/\mathfrak{p}$ in $V'/\mathfrak{m}'$ is a finitely generated

$A/\mathfrak{p}$ -module, since clearly $V/\mathfrak{m}$ is the field of fractions of $A/\mathfrak{p}$. Therefore $A'/\mathfrak{m}' \cap A'$ is contained in a finitely generated $A/\mathfrak{p}$ -module, and is hence itself finitely generated $A/\mathfrak{p}$ -module (A is noetherian). Therefore $A'/\mathfrak{m}' \cap A'$ is a finitely generated A-module, and c) is proved.

Let now $\widehat{A'}$ denote the completion of A' in the xA'-adic topology which, by b) is Hausdorff. Therefore we have that $\widehat{A'}$ contains an isomorphic copy of A', and we identify the two, i.e we have $A' \subset \widehat{A'}$. By statement 6) at the beginning of section 6A we have $\widehat{A'}/x\widehat{A'} \simeq A'/xA'$, and in the proof of c) we actually showed that A'/xA' is a finitely generated A/xA-module. Since A is complete and Hausdorff in the xA-adic topology, we can apply part ii) of Proposition 14 of B.C.A., Chapter III, §2, no 11, and obtain that $\widehat{A'}$ is a finitely generated A-module. Therefore $A' \subset \widehat{A'}$ is also finitely generated over A, and the lemma is proved.

We now proceed with the proof of theorem 6.4, namely that every complete noetherian local domain is Japanese.

By Cohen's Structure theorem, since A is an integral domain, A contains a ring B which is regular and such that A is a finitely generated B-module. Therefore A is integral over B, and hence it suffices to prove that B is Japanese, since for every finite extension L of the field of fractions K of A we have $A'_L = B'_L$, and L is a finite extension of the field of fractions F of B. Therefore it suffices to prove the theorem with the additional assumption that A is regular.

We proceed by induction on n = dim(A). If n = 0, since A

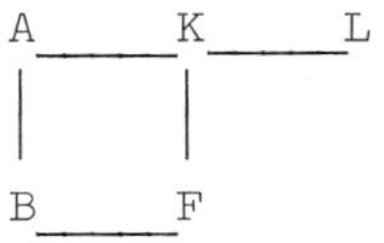

is integral, it follows that A is a field, trivially a Japanese ring. Assume $n > 0$ and let $x \in A$ be an A-regular element, $x \notin \mathfrak{m}^2$. Then A/xA is again regular (Corollary 4.2) and complete and $\dim(A/xA) = n-1$. Since A/xA is regular, xA is a prime ideal. By the induction assumption A/xA is Japanese. Furthermore, A being complete and Hausdorff in the $\mathfrak{m}$-adic topology, it is so a fortiori in the xA-adic topology. Since A is regular, it is integrally closed, and by lemma 6.2 A is Japanese. The theorem is proved.

<u>Corollary 6.1</u>. Let A be a complete, local, noetherian integral domain, K the field of fractions of A, K' a finite field extension of K. The integral closure A' of A in K' is a local ring.

<u>Proof</u>. By theorem 6.4 A' is a finitely generated A-module. Therefore A' is complete in the $\mathfrak{m}A'$-adic topology (B.C.A. Chapter III, §2, no 12, Corollary 1), and semi-local (B.C.A. Chapter IV, §2, no 5, Corollary 3), and $\mathfrak{m}A'$ is an ideal of definition of A'. Therefore the $\mathfrak{m}A'$-adic topology on A' is equivalent to the $\mathfrak{r}$-adic topology, where $\mathfrak{r}$ denotes the radical of A'. By proposition 18 of B.C.A., Chapter III, §2, no 13, (applied to A') we have $A' = \prod_{i=1}^{q} A'_i$, where each A'_i is a local ring, $i = 1,\dots,q$. Since A' is an integral domain, $q = 1$ and A' is a local ring, q.e.d.

If A is a noetherian, local, integral domain, it need not

be a Japanese ring. However, A is Japanese if two certain conditions hold for the completion $\hat{A}$ of A. Namely

Proposition 6.4. Let A be a noetherian local, integral domain, $\hat{A}$ the completion of A in the $\mathfrak{m}$-adic topology, K the field of fractions of A, K' a finite field extension of K, A' the integral closure of A in K'. Let R be the total ring of fractions of $\hat{A}$. If

i) $\hat{A}$ is reduced

ii) $R \otimes_K K'$ is reduced

then A' is a finitely generated A-module.

Proof: Let $\mathfrak{p}_1, \ldots, \mathfrak{p}_t$ be the minimal prime ideals of $\hat{A}$, and let L_i be the field of fractions of $B_i = \hat{A}/\mathfrak{p}_i$, i=1,...,t. Since $\hat{A}$ is reduced we have $\bigcap_{i=1}^{t} \mathfrak{p}_i = (0)$ and a sequence of inclusions

$$\hat{A} \to \prod B_i \to \prod L_i$$

with

$$R = \prod L_i .$$

Now let $A_1 = \hat{A}$, $A'_1 = A' \otimes_A A_1$, $K'_1 = K' \otimes_A A_1$, $K_1 = K \otimes_A A_1$. We therefore have $K'_1 = K' \otimes_K K_1$. Since A_1 is a faithfully flat A-module, it suffices to prove that A'_1 is a finitely generated A_1-module. Furthermore, again by the flatness of A_1 over A we have $A'_1 \subset K'_1$. Finally, letting S denote the multiplicatively closed subset of A consisting of the non zero divisors of A, we clearly have $K = S^{-1}A$, and $K_1 = S^{-1}A \otimes_A A_1 = S^{-1}A_1$, since S consists of non zero divisors of A_1 also. Clearly $S^{-1}A_1 \subset R$, whence $K_1 \subset R$. We therefore have the inclusion diagram

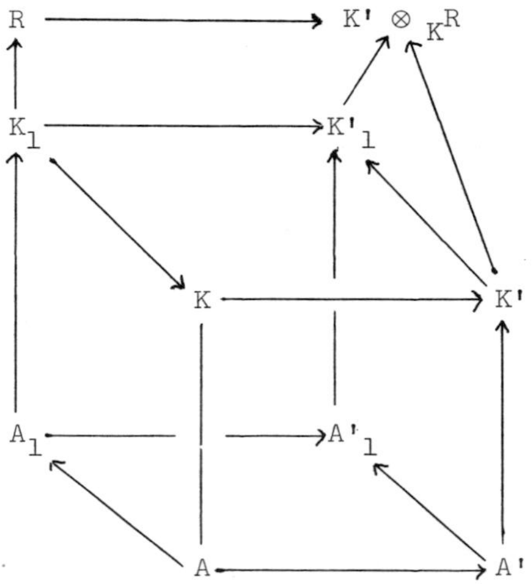

where $K'_1 \subset K' \otimes_K R$ is seen from $K_1 \subset R$ and the flatness of K' over K.

By proposition 5 of B.C.A., Chapter V, §1, no 2, A'_1 is integral over A_1, and is therefore contained in the integral closure C of A_1 in $K' \otimes_K R$.

If $a \in A$ is not a zero divisor, then a is not a zero divisor in A_1. From this we see that the L_i's are vector spaces over K. Since $R = \prod L_i$, we have $K' \otimes_K R = \prod K' \otimes_K L_i$ and, since $K' \otimes_K R$ is reduced, so are the $K' \otimes_K L_i$, $i = 1,\ldots,t$. Furthermore, since $[K':K] < \infty$, $K' \otimes_K L_i$ is finitely generated over L_i, $i = 1,\ldots,t$. Since $K' \otimes_K L_i$ has no nilpotent elements and, again, $[K':K] < \infty$, $K' \otimes_K L_i$ is a product $\prod_j M_{ij}$, where the M_{ij} are fields, which are actually finite field extensions of L_i. Therefore the integral closure B'_i of B_i in $K' \otimes_K L_i$ is, by theorem 6.4, a finitely generated B_i-module, $i = 1,\ldots,t$, and hence a finitely generated A_1-module. Since A'_1 is integral over A_1 we have $A'_1 \subset \prod_{i=1}^{t} B'_i$, and therefore A'_1, being contained in a finitely generated A_1-module, is itself a finitely generated A_1-module, and the proposition is proved.

Theorem 6.5. Let A be a reduced noetherian local ring with geometrically regular formal fibers. Then:

1) $\hat{A}$ is reduced
2) The integral closure A' of A in its total ring of fractions is a finitely generated A-module
3) The completion $\widehat{A'}$ of A' is isomorphic to the integral closure of $\hat{A}$ in its total ring of fractions
4) There exists a 1-1 correspondence between the maximal ideals of A' and the minimal prime ideals of $\hat{A}$ given by

$$\widehat{A'_{\mathfrak{m}}} \simeq \hat{A}/\mathfrak{q}$$

where $\mathfrak{m}$ is a maximal ideal in A' and $\mathfrak{q}$ the corresponding minimal prime ideal in $\hat{A}$.

Proof: 1) This is a direct result of theorem 5.7. Note that here we only need the formal fibers to be regular.

2) Let $\mathfrak{p}_i$, $i = 1,\ldots,t$ be the minimal prime ideals of A,

and let $B_i = A/\mathfrak{p}_i$, $i = 1,\ldots,t$.

We assert that $\widehat{B_i}$ is reduced, $i = 1,\ldots,t$. In fact, let $\widehat{B_i}/\mathfrak{q}\widehat{B_i}$, $\mathfrak{q} \in \mathrm{Spec}(B_i)$ be a formal fiber of B_i. Then, letting $\mathfrak{p}$ denote the unique prime ideal of A corresponding to $\mathfrak{q}$ we have $\widehat{B_i}/\mathfrak{q}\widehat{B_i} \simeq \widehat{A}/\mathfrak{p}\widehat{A}$. I.e. that the formal fibers of B_i are isomorphic to formal fibers of A. As B_i is reduced, by proposition 5.7, $\widehat{B_i}$ is reduced, $i = 1,\ldots,t$. If L_i denotes the field of fractions of B_i, $i = 1,\ldots,t$, then $A \subset \prod_i B_i \subset \prod_i L_i$. Apply proposition 6.4, with $K = K' = L_i$. It follows that the integral closure B'_i of B_i in L_i is a finitely generated B_i-module, hence a finitely generated A-module. Now clearly $\prod_i L_i$ is the total ring of fractions of A, whence $A' = \prod B'_i$, and 2) is proved.

3) We let $X = \mathrm{Spec}(\widehat{A})$, $Y = \mathrm{Spec}(A)$, $Z = \mathrm{Spec}(A')$. Then we have canonical morphisms $\varphi : X \to Y$, $\Psi : Z \to Y$.

By 2) A' is a finitely generated A-module, and by part (ii) of Theorem 3 of B.C.A., Chapter III, §3, no 4, $\widehat{A'} \simeq \widehat{A} \otimes_A A'$. Therefore, if we let $W = \mathrm{Spec}\,\widehat{A'}$ we have the commutative diagram

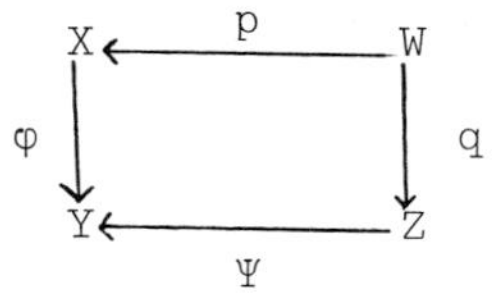

Let $w \in W$, $z = q(w)$, $y = \Psi(z)$, $x = p(w)$. Then $\varphi(x) = y$ and

$$O_x \otimes_{O_y} k(z) = (O_x \otimes_{O_y} k(y)) \otimes_{k(y)} k(z)$$

is the local ring of w in $q^{-1}(z)$.
Since A' is a finitely generated A-module, it follows $[k(z):k(y)] < \infty$, and since $O_x \otimes_{O_y} k(y)$ is geometrically regular, so is $O_x \otimes_{O_y} k(z)$. Therefore the formal fibers of A' are geometrically regular. Let $\mathfrak{m}_1, \ldots, \mathfrak{m}_t$ denote the maximal ideals of A' (A' is semi-local). By the corollary to proposition 19 of B.C.A., Chapter III, §2, no 13, $\widehat{A'} = \prod_j \widehat{A'_{\mathfrak{m}_j}}$. Therefore, since A' has geometrically regular formal fibers, so do the $A'_{\mathfrak{m}_j}$, $j = 1, \ldots, t$.

Since A' is normal and has (geometrically) regular formal fibers, it follows from theorem 5.7 that $\widehat{A'}$ is normal. Since $\widehat{A}$ if faithfully flat, over A, the inclusions $A \subset A' \subset R$ imply, by tensoring with $\widehat{A}$, the inclusion relations $\widehat{A} \subset \widehat{A'} \subset R \otimes_A \widehat{A}$. Now $R \otimes_A \widehat{A}$ is clearly contained in the total ring of fractions R" of $\widehat{A}$. Therefore $\widehat{A'}$ is a normal ring containing $\widehat{A}$ and contained in the total ring of fractions of $\widehat{A}$. It follows that $\widehat{A'}$ is the normalization of $\widehat{A}$ in R", and 3) is proved.

4) With the same notations as in the proof of 3), we have $\widehat{A'} = \prod_{j=1}^{t} \widehat{A'_{\mathfrak{m}_j}}$. Let $\mathfrak{q}_1, \ldots, \mathfrak{q}_s$ denote the minimal prime ideals of $\widehat{A}$. Since $\widehat{A}$ is reduced, we have the inclusions $\widehat{A} \subset \prod_{i=1}^{s} \widehat{A}/\mathfrak{q}_i \subset R''$. It follows that the integral closure of $\widehat{A}$ in R" is given by $\prod_{i=1}^{s} B_i$, where B_i denotes the integral closure

of $\widehat{A}/\mathfrak{q}_i$ in its field of fractions. By corollary 6.1, B_i is a local ring, i = 1,...,s, and by 3)

$$\prod_{j=1}^{t} \widehat{A'_{\mathfrak{m}_j}} = \widehat{A'} = \prod_{i=1}^{s} B_i$$

Therefore s = t, and up to a reordering $\widehat{A'_{\mathfrak{m}_j}} = (\widehat{A}/\mathfrak{q}_j)'$. The theorem is proved.

We complete this work with a definition and a theorem of Grothendieck, which we shall leave unproved.

Definition 6.4. A noetherian local ring A is said to be excellent if

i) A has geometrically regular formal fibers

ii) Every finitely generated A algebra is catenary (i.e. A is universally catenary)

Theorem 6.6. (Grothendieck) Let A be an excellent local ring. Then every localization of a finitely generated algebra over A is excellent. (E.G.A., IV, 7.4.4).

Date Due

11 Oct 68 F			
MAY 1 6 1973			